D0349391
FREDDY the FEARLESS FLY
PANSY POTTER
MUSSO the WOP
MORGYN the MIGHTY
BING-BANG BENNY
BLACK BOB
KORKY the CAT
LITTLE PLUM
DINAH MO
BILLY WHIZZ

The Dandy and The Beano
Fifty Golden Years

Printed and Published in Great Britain by D.C. Thomson & Co., Ltd.,
185 Fleet Street, London, EC4A 2HS.

ISBN 0 85116 384 X

(Certain stories do not appear exactly, as originally published.)

half-century of The DANDY and The BEANO! This, surely is a milestone in comic history. Indeed, it is something more than that — almost a milestone in BRITISH history, so well-known and loved are both comics. From the late thirties to the present day, countless million readers, young and not-so-young, have avidly followed the adventures of the great British cartoon characters.

When the idea of publishing this Golden Jubilee edition was first raised, no great hint of the ensuing problems could be guessed at. However, the first major snag was, very soon, very apparent. There was just *too much material.* There was, indeed, such an over-abundance of riches, that at one point, estimates of 100 volumes, akin to a comic version of Encyclopaedia Britannica began to appear distinctly possible. This in its turn led to the most painful decision of all. What could be left out, which characters should be omitted, who and what would be denied space in this 50-year celebration of fun?

To those readers whose favourite memories have been pruned from the following pages, my humble apologies. The contents of the book are, I hope, a fair representation of the best tales of their time, the best loved humorous characters and of the enduring national figures such as Desperate Dan.

Big Eggo, Korky the Cat, Lord Snooty and his Gang, Morgyn the Mighty, Biffo the Bear, Jack Flash, Black Bob, Jimmy (and His Magic Patch) Watson, General 'Jumbo' Johnson, Desperate Dan, Dennis the Menace, Shipwrecked Circus, The Bash Street Kids, Our Gang . . . the names roll off the tongue like a regiment's battle honours. Talking of battle honours, how many can remember wartime favourites Addie and Hermy or Musso, characters born of the great British ability to poke fun at its troubles in the dark days of World War II?

My own over-riding childhood memories of the comics, are of anxious moments awaiting the paper delivery boy, then tearing the precious cargo from within its wrapper of some barely glanced-at newspaper, a newspaper which would be enveloping someone's fish 'n' chips long, long before the week's DANDY and BEANO contents had been digested by Mum, Dad, brother and sister.

However, like the aforementioned pruning of material, I too must curb my tendency to indulge in too many personal reminiscences. Suffice to say, I hope this "50 Golden Years" volume will give you as much pleasure to read as it gave me to produce.

The Editor

FIRST DAY COVER

Nº1 EXPRESS WHISTLER FREE INSIDE

DECEMBER 4th. 1937

IF The DANDY editor had known that his new comic would be going strong 50 years on, he might have arranged a fanfare of trumpets for that first issue, rather than the "Express Whistler" — the gift that was enclosed in every copy.

The cheerful bellboy notched up an impressive 23 years service, smiling out at DANDY readers, from his perch beside the title, until his retiral in October 1960.

But **Korky the Cat** went on to prove he really does have nine lives. Britain's most famous feline is now as old as the comic itself.

Another notable feature is the "silent movie" storylines of the early **Korky** stories. DANDY readers weren't to enjoy his cat chat until 1942.

Comics have always been value-for-money funnies. Two old pennies bought the first DANDY, an amount worth less than a modern one pence piece.

FIRST DAY COVER

MEET **Big Eggo,** page one bird in the early days of The BEANO.

Loveable, eat-anything **Eggo** and his BEANO comic mates were an instant success, with readers all over Britain scrambling to buy the new, laugh-a-minute publication. Even so, few people realised then that BEANO number one was to be the birth of a legend.

We suspect too, that **Big Eggo** himself would have laid an egg if he'd realised that ten years later he'd be winging his way off the cover of the now famous comic! His replacement? One of the all-time comic greats — **Biffo The Bear.**

As for the comic itself, it has gone from strength to strength since first hitting the streets in 1938.

Eyes right for an eyeful of the first cover. Eyes peeled for some great moments from BEANO'S fifty glorious years (so far!) on the following pages . . .

JULY 30th. 1938

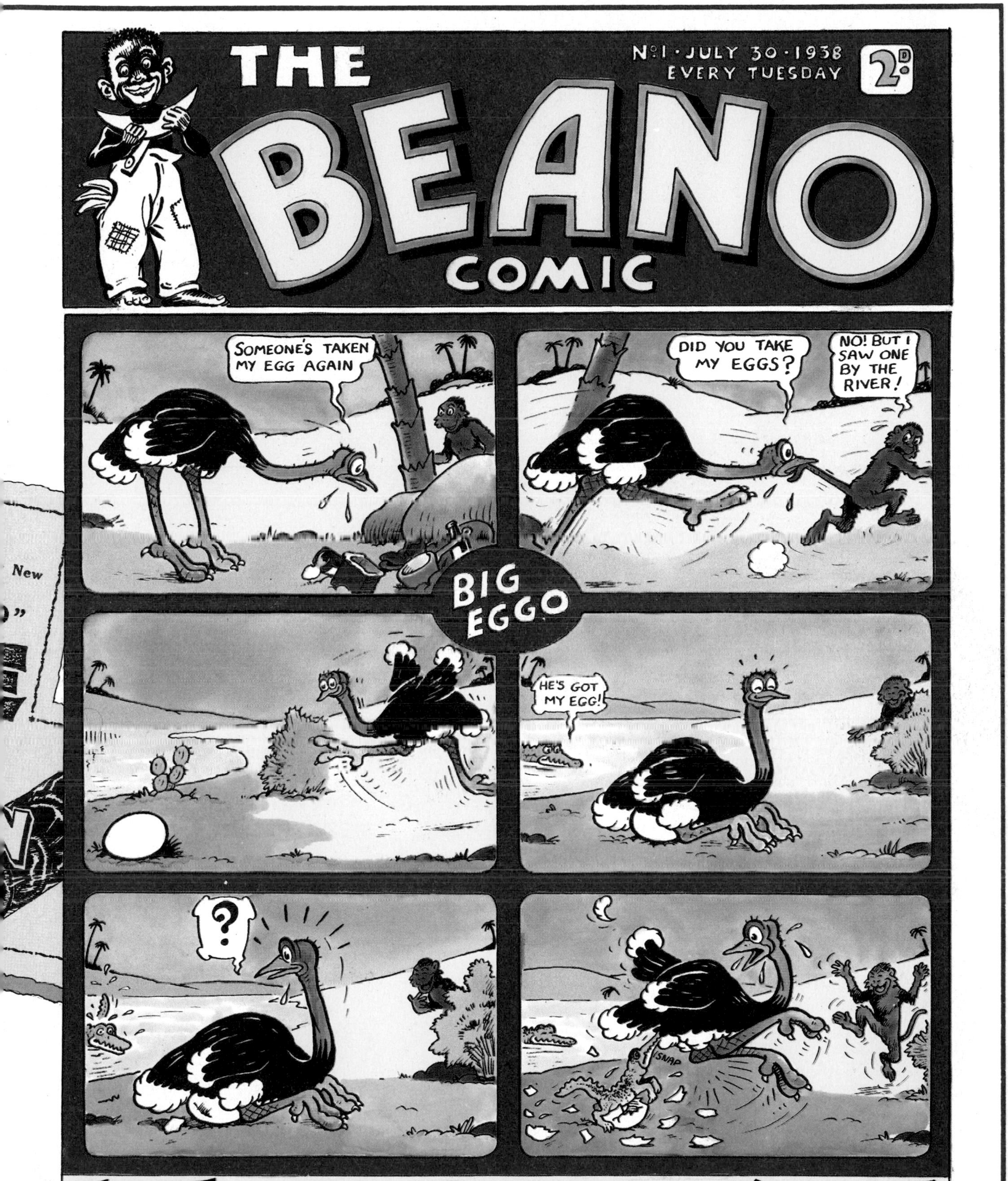

SOMEONE'S TAKEN MY EGG AGAIN

DID YOU TAKE MY EGGS?

NO! BUT I SAW ONE BY THE RIVER!

BIG EGGO

HE'S GOT MY EGG!

?

SNAP

FREE INSIDE

WHOOPEE MASK

50 GOLDEN YEARS

WHAT DOES MIKE READ?

THE BEANO, OF COURSE

TV star, radio personality and comic fan **Mike Read** has given lots of "plugs" to his favourite comics over the years.

That's why he was so delighted when he found a new kind of fame by actually appearing in the pages of BEANO!

What's more, as you can see from the pic, man of all talents Mike, who numbers poetry, writing musicals and compiling quiz games amongst his many activities, has even done some BEANO-style modelling in his time.

Mike proudly wears his "designer" jersey. Styled by Dennis? Knitted by Softy Walter?

Mike's second appearance in BEANO — giving a helping hand to another famous personality, Dennis the Menace.

DENNIS the MENACE
AND ~~GNASHER~~
CONTINUED FROM FRONT PAGE

Later—
RECORDING STUDIO
GOT TIME TO DO A GNASHER APPEAL, MIKE READ?

...I HAVE!
I'M A BEANO GNASHER SPOTTER

JOIN THE GNATIONAL GNASHER SEARCH...

Later—
NOW HERE'S WHAT TO DO IF YOU SUSPECT GNASHER'S NEAR YOUR HOUSE...

...BUILD A GNASHER TRAP. HERE'S HOW.

COVER THE HOLE WITH LEAVES!

STARQUOTE

"I was thrilled when I was featured in The BEANO. It's one of my favourites."

TELL ME A STORY, GRANDPA!
CERTAINLY, DEAR CHILD!
ONCE UPON A TIME, THERE WERE NO COMICS!
OOH!
In the garden of Eden—
PSSST! FANCY AN APPLE, DUCKY?
I'D RATHER HAVE A DANDY OR A BEANO!
SORRY, LUV! THEY AIN'T BEEN INVENTED YET!
Later, in a cave—
CHIP!
I'M GOING TO INVENT THE FIRST COMIC!
STOP WASTING YOUR TIME AND GET BUSY INVENTING THE WHEEL!
WHACK!
1492 Christopher Columbus, explorer.
I GO TO DISCOVER YE DANDY AND YE BEANO!
YOU'VE GOT TO DISCOVER AMERICA FIRST, CHRIS!
William Caxton inventor of the first printing machine.
GOOD! NOW I'LL BE ABLE TO PRINT THE DANDY AND THE BEANO!
YE PRINTING INK
Venerable Bede— Grumphy historian—
NO, WILLIAM! YOU WILL PRINT THE DOOMSDAY BOOK INSTEAD!
COR! WOT A DRAG!
BUT AT LAST IN 1937 AND 1938 THE DANDY AND BEANO WERE INVENTED— AND WE ALL LIVED HAPPILY EVER AFTER!
ANY MORE SUPER STORIES, GRANDPA?
TICKLE!
YES — JUST TURN THE PAGE, AND READ ALL ABOUT IT!

COMIC stars for fifty years, **Korky the Cat** and **Lord Snooty** can look right back to the early days of DANDY and BEANO — when an early television set could be bought for around twenty-seven pounds and an ingenious inventor had just come up with a great idea for the kitchen — the musical kettle which whistled when it boiled!

They can also look back to some great comic characters who shared the early pages of the comic with them.

Characters like **Wig and Wam** and **Contrary Mary** have long since disappeared from BEANO and DANDY, but they were great fun in their day . . .

...THE EARLY DAYS

FREDDY THE FEARLESS FLY

DANDY 19th FEBRUARY, 1938

FLIPPY THE SEA-SERPENT

DANDY 30th APRIL, 1938

WIG AND WAM

DANDY 8th JANUARY, 1938

PODGE

DANDY 8th JANUARY, 1938

MUGG MUGGINS

DANDY 8th JANUARY, 1938

GOOD KING COKE

BEANO 13th MAY, 1939

HELPFUL HENRY

BEANO 25th FEBRUARY, 1939

WEE PEEM

BEANO 13th MAY, 1939

CONTRARY MARY

BEANO 25th FEBRUARY, 1939

DEEP-DOWN DADDY NEPTUNE

BEANO 30th DECEMBER, 1939

KEYHOLE CILLA

KEYHOLE KATE, the nosiest girl in the history of comics, first started readers chuckling in the very first issue of DANDY, but although Kate's no longer peering through keyholes in the pages of the comic, TV star **Cilla Black,** remembers her adventures very well indeed — for one special reason . . .

Says Cilla, "I loved the DANDY and the BEANO as a child. When I was at school, I was so painfully thin, they used to call me **Keyhole Kate!**"

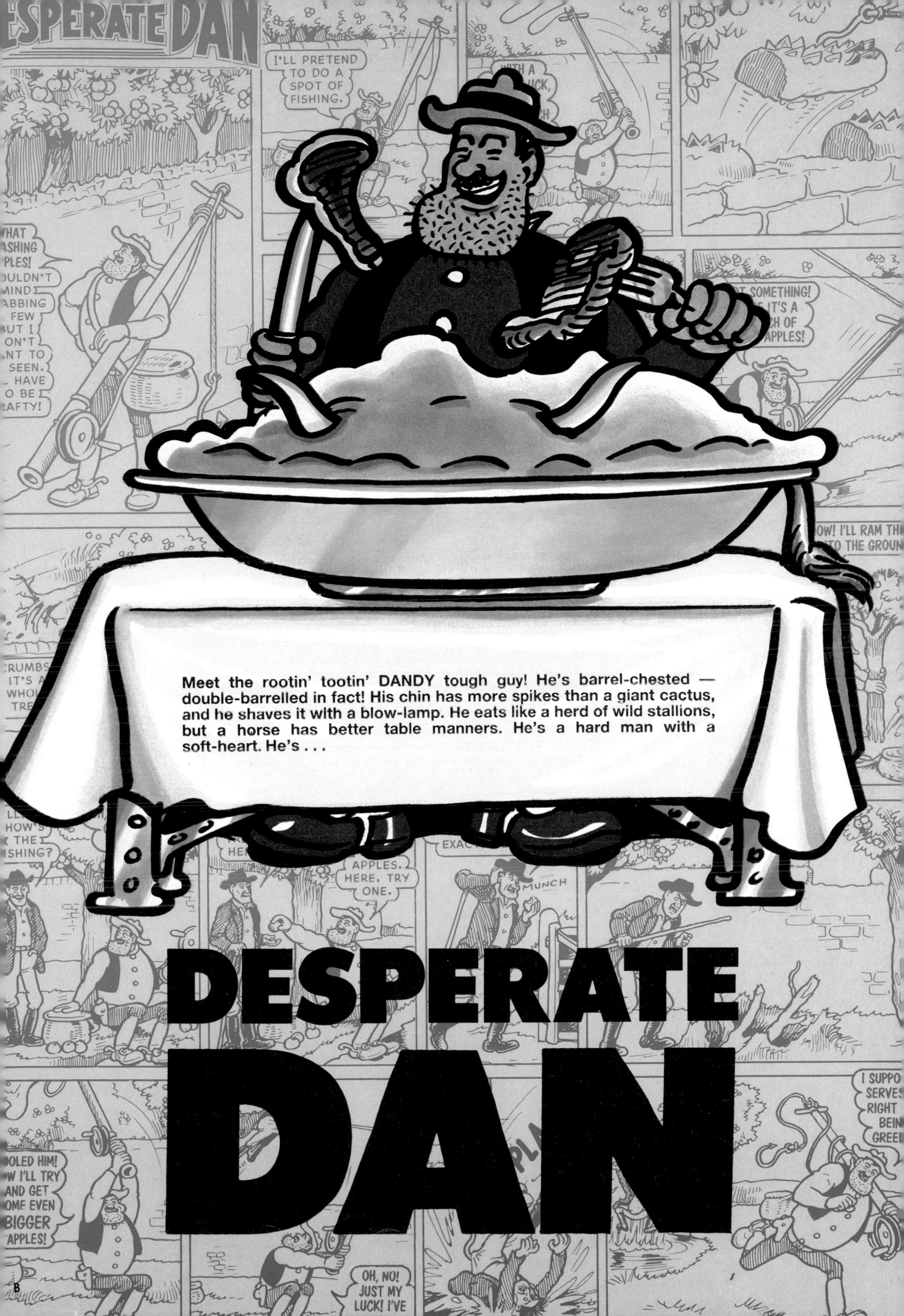

DESPERATE DAN
I'LL PRETEND TO DO A SPOT OF FISHING.
Meet the rootin' tootin' DANDY tough guy! He's barrel-chested — double-barrelled in fact! His chin has more spikes than a giant cactus, and he shaves it with a blow-lamp. He eats like a herd of wild stallions, but a horse has better table manners. He's a hard man with a soft-heart. He's . . .
APPLES. HERE, TRY ONE.
MUNCH
DESPERATE DAN
OH, NO! JUST MY LUCK! I'VE

WAY DOWN IN TEXAS WE SAY OLD TIMERS ARE "AS OLD AS THE HILLS". WELL, SHUCKS, MAYBE I AM A FEW YEARS YOUNGER THAN THE ROCKIES, BUT I'VE BEEN AROUND AS LONG AS THE DANDY. TAKE A LOOK BELOW AND YOU'LL SEE MY VERY FIRST STORY FROM 4TH DECEMBER, 1937. I PACKED A POWERFUL PUNCH EVEN BACK THEN!

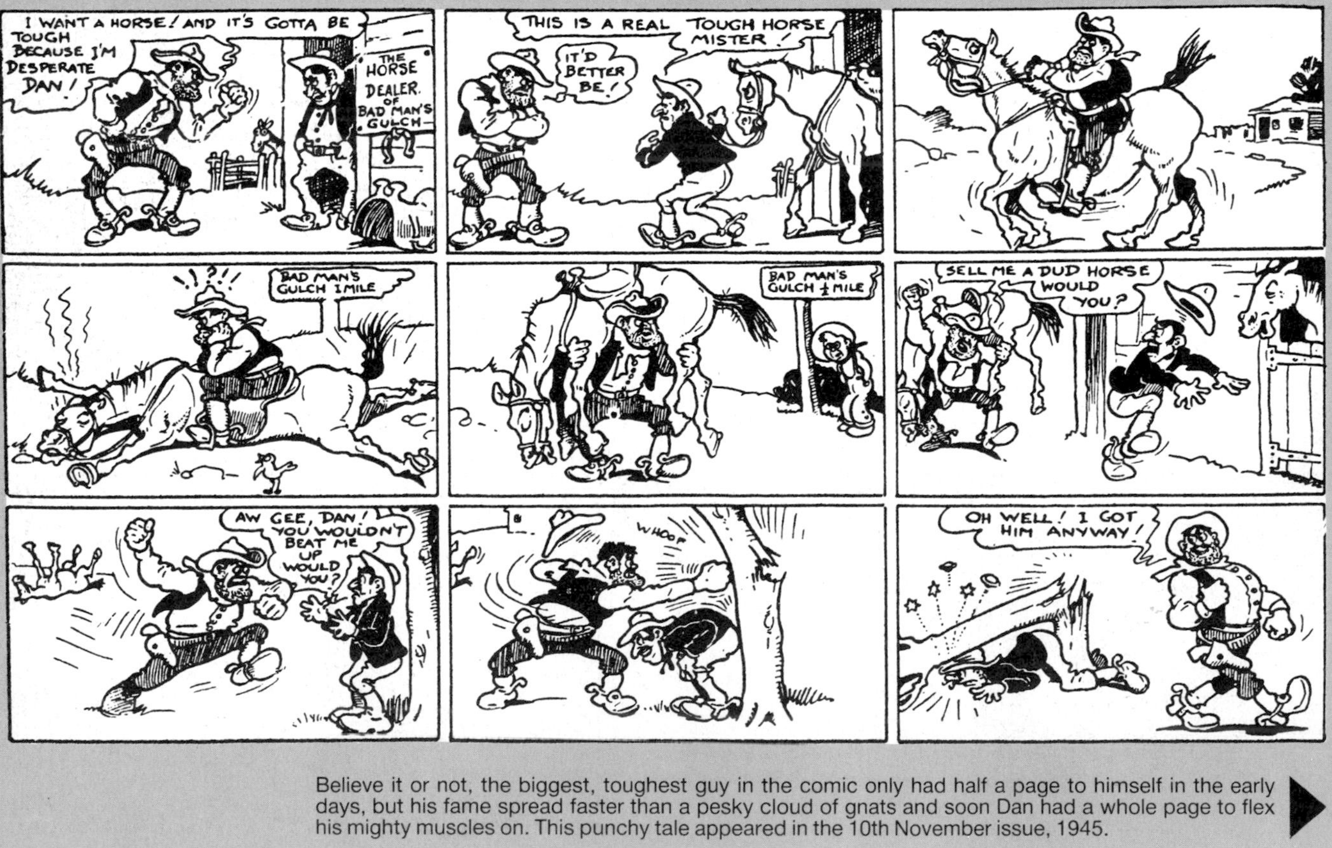

I WANT A HORSE! AND IT'S GOTTA BE TOUGH BECAUSE I'M DESPERATE DAN!
THE HORSE DEALER OF BAD MAN'S GULCH
THIS IS A REAL TOUGH HORSE MISTER!
IT'D BETTER BE!
!?!
BAD MAN'S GULCH 1 MILE
BAD MAN'S GULCH ½ MILE
SELL ME A DUD HORSE WOULD YOU?
AW GEE, DAN! YOU WOULDN'T BEAT ME UP WOULD YOU?
WHOOP
OH WELL! I GOT HIM ANYWAY!

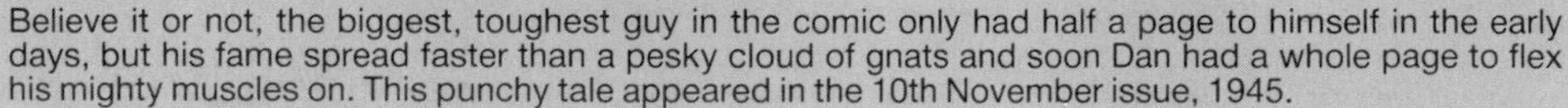

Believe it or not, the biggest, toughest guy in the comic only had half a page to himself in the early days, but his fame spread faster than a pesky cloud of gnats and soon Dan had a whole page to flex his mighty muscles on. This punchy tale appeared in the 10th November issue, 1945.

HERE'S HOW TO SHOW YOU'RE TOUGH, DAN! FIGHT OUR CHAMP AND IF YOU BEAT HIM YOU GET £5
BRING HIM ALONG BOYS! I'LL TWIST HIS TONSILS ROUND HIS TOE-NAILS TWICE.

I'D BETTER DO A SPOT OF TRAINING! THIS NOTICE SHOULD HELP ME TO GET SOME SCRAPPING PRACTICE!
NOTICE – SPARRING PARTNERS WANTED APPLY D. DAN PAY 5/- PER HOUR – (IF YOU'RE STILL ALIVE TO COLLECT IT)

COME TO UNCLE DANNY, MY LITTLE LADS. I'LL SOON TOUGHEN UP WITH YOU FELLOWS!
JUST WAIT, YOU BIG STIFF. WE'LL KNOCK YOUR NOSE AMONG YOUR HAIR.
SPARRING PARTNER

THEY FLY THROUGH THE AIR WITH THE GREATEST OF EASE.—AND LAND WITH A CRASH ON THEIR ELBOWS AND KNEES!
WOW! I THOUGHT WE WERE TO BE SPARRING PARTNERS BUT I FEEL MORE LIKE A SPITFIRE PILOT!

ACCEPT THIS LITTLE SOMETHING! THESE MEN WILL MAKE FINE SANDWICH-BOARDS TO ADVERTISE MY NERVE TONIC!
BOY! THERE'S MONEY IN THIS BOXING GAME.
THEY KNOX'S BUY A
DIDN'T NERVE BOTTLE
TAKE TONIC NOW

DROP THIS STEAM-HAMMER ON MY CHIN BUDDY! I'LL HAVE TO TOUGHEN UP MY JAWBONE A BIT IF I'M TO FIGHT THE CHAMP!
I HOPE I DON'T HURT YOU MUCH, DAN!

ACKLING, OYOTES! 'VE BUST THE TEAM-HAMMER: GUESS 'LL HAVE O FIND OMETHING ELSE TO RACTICE AKING UNCHES ON THE JAW WITH.
SUFFERING CAT-FISH! MY HAMMER'S RUINED!
CRASH

IF I DIVE INTO THIS EMPTY SWIMMING POOL, THAT OUGHT TO TOUGHEN UP MY JAW!

GROWLING GRIZZLIES! I'M GOING THROUGH TO AUSTRALIA!
CRASH

COME ON, STEAM SHOVEL! IT'S TIME
ME OUT.
SLOW!

HIS VINDMILL IS IKE BEING UNCHED ON HE CHIN. T LAST 'VE FOUND OMETHING TO GET ME IN GOOD TRIM!

I FEEL FINE NOW! THESE WINDMILLS SURE ARE FINE FOR TRAINING.
YOU MAY FEEL FINE, BUT THE WINDMILLS DON'T.

OUT OF THE WAY, MIDGET. WHY DON'T YOU FIND YOURSELF A NICE PIECE OF FLYPAPER TO GET STUCK ON?
GEE, OUR MAN'S NEVER GOING TO WIN UNLESS WE FIND SOME WAY TO FIX DAN!

HAVEN'T HE HEART O FINISH THIS ITTLE BOY OFF!
THIS PEPPER WILL FIX DANNY ALL RIGHT. WHILE HE'S SNEEZING OUR CHAMP WILL BE ABLE TO SOCK HIM IN THE TUMMY!

WOW! HELP! I'M GOING TO SNEEZE! SOMETHING'S TICKLING MY SCHNOZZLE!
A-A-A TISHOO

GALLOPING GUN-BELTS! I'VE BLOWN EVERYONE AWAY WITH MY SNEEZING, BUT THEY'VE LEFT ME ALL THE PRIZE-MONEY. THERE MUST BE PLENTY OF IT IF IT WAS TOO HEAVY TO BLOW AWAY!
SAFE
PRIZE MONEY

Meet the family! There's my Aunt Aggie and young Danny and Katey, my nephew and niece. No wonder everyone's smiling. We're off to the beach and when the transport is Dan-powered it doesn't cost a cent for petrol.

When Aunt Aggie saw my hiking rucksack she said I was taking everything but the kitchen sink. She was wrong! I did remember to pack the kitchen sink!

I'm a musical guy, but I've such powerful puff no other musician can stand the noise. I solved that problem with "Desperate Dan's One-Man-Band".

Some guy told me ostriches can't fly, so I reckoned all they needed was a few lessons, and yours truly was happy to oblige.

TO CACTUSVILLE

and Desperate Dan

When the sheriff asked for my help because of illness I thought his deputy was poorly. I found out too late, it was his hoss!

Nothing but a blow-lamp can shift the stubble from my chin and even that doesn't shave me clean. But it ain't all bad! When I entered the "Stubbliest Chin In Texas Contest", I won on points.

Aunt Aggie was always moanin' an' groanin' about the long walk to the store, but I sure quietened her down the day I brought the store to her! I put it back later, of course.

Folks reckon we're rough and ready down Cactusville way, but that just ain't true! What could be more refined than me an' my buddy, Dog-Ears Montana, taking afternoon tea?

THANKS to his bulging biceps, Dan's rarely had to draw his six-gun during his fifty years of Wild West life. But any self-respecting cowboy would feel naked without his pistol, and our hero was no exception in this story from 10th December, 1983.

SHERIFF
THERE'S THAT PESKY RACOON THAT ATE ONE OF MY COW-PIES!

SHERIFF
TAKE THAT! . . . PAH! MISSED.
SQUIRT!
SQUEEZE!
LEAP!

CRASH!
YAH!
WHOOSH!

hen—
EVEN WATER PISTOLS ARE BANNED, DAN! NOW COME AND HELP ME GUARD THE CHECKPOINT!

SORRY! YOU CAN'T BRING THAT CANNON INTO TOWN!
HMM!
HUMAN CANNONBALL
CIRCUS
STOP! CHECKPOINT
GUNS
BUT THE HUMAN CANNONBALL IS OUR STAR ATTRACTION!

WHOOSH!

SHUCKS! SOMETIMES I DON'T KNOW MY OWN STRENGTH!

GET ME DOWN!

THE GOVERNOR'S VISITING CACTUSVILLE, BUT SINCE WE'VE BANNED GUNS WE CAN'T GIVE HIM A TWENTY-ONE GUN SALUTE!
I'LL BURST TWENTY-ONE PAPER BAGS, MAYOR! THE BANGS WILL SOUND JUST LIKE CANNON SHOTS!

ULP! MAYBE I SHOULD HAVE TAKEN THE TOMATOES OUT OF THE BAGS FIRST!
LEAP!
BANG! BANG!
SPLATTER!
BANG! BANG!
BANG! BANG!
UGH!

Later—
I WONDER WHO'S AT MY DOOR!
KNOCK! KNOCK!

TAKE THESE, DAN! YOU CAN'T BE ANY MORE DANGEROUS WITH GUNS THAN YOU'VE BEEN WITHOUT THEM!
TIP!

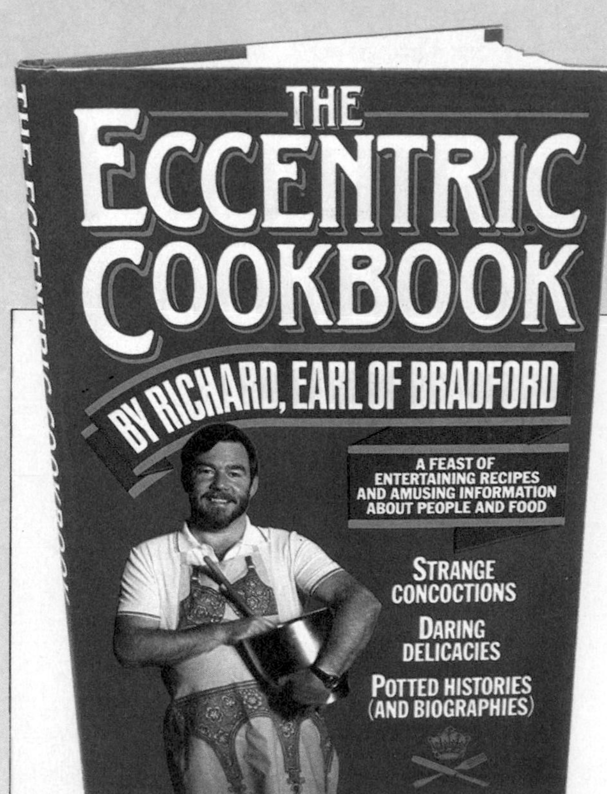

DAN'S RECIPE FOR SUCCESS

DESPERATE DAN'S COW-PIE

Take one cow, polish horns, launder tail and place in large pie dish. Dish should be first rubbed thoroughly with grizzly-bear grease and bear returned carefully to its cave. *Pastry* — Empty three sacks of flour into a cement mixer. Add six ostrich eggs and a horse-trough of water. Mix thoroughly. Roll out pastry with road roller, driven carefully at 3 mph. (Cover cow with pastry.) Garnish with a pint of owlhoot juice (Spare pastry can be kept for multifarious uses, such as filling pot-holes in the road.) Bake in a moderately hot volcano till crust turns a golden black! May be served with granite chips and fresh cactus shoots. Essence of polecat will add a certain piquancy to gravy. Season to taste — or take with a large pinch of salt!

Serves five large families or one Desperate Dan.

THE comic world's best kept secret is out! **Desperate Dan** has been persuaded to share the recipe for his famous cow-pies.

How did it happen? Well, The Earl of Bradford felt that his "Eccentric Cookbook" full of weird and wonderful recipes, wouldn't be complete without Dan's delicacy, and shucks, the DANDY strongman couldn't say no to an English earl.

So here it is, the dish for Dan-sized appetites! And if you're still wondering if cow-pies really do keep up Dan's strength, just take a look below!

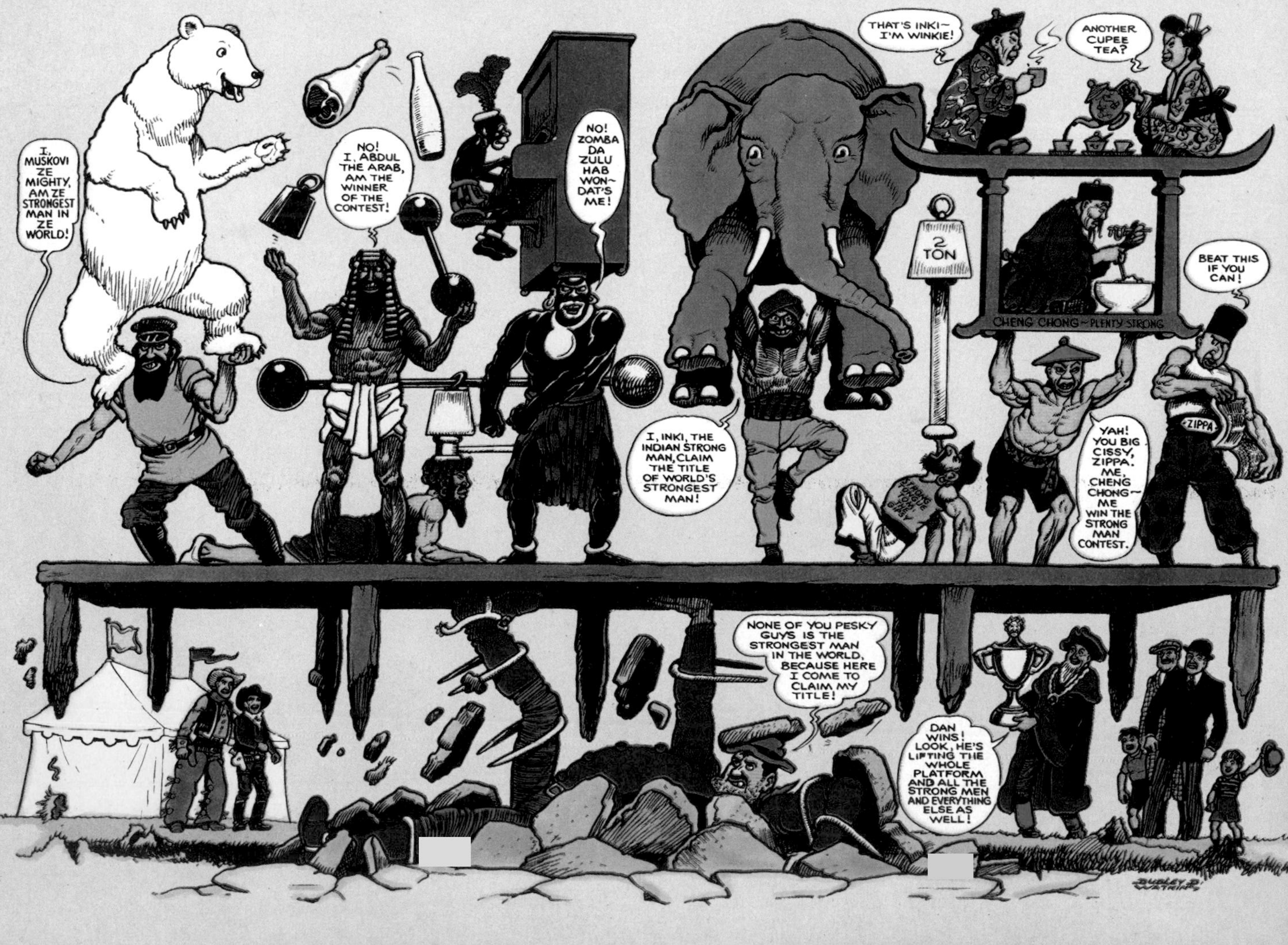

CONGRATULATIONS

AS you might expect, those stars of the comic world BEANO and DANDY can count lots of star names amongst their greatest fans.
The magic of the famous twosome has even filtered through the hallowed walls of 10 Downing Street!

10 DOWNING STREET

THE PRIME MINISTER

Congratulations on the 50th Anniversary of "The Dandy" and "The Beano".

These must be among the world's most famous and most loved comics.

Over the years they have given enjoyment to countless numbers of children and the characters in their pages - such as "Desperate Dan" and "Minnie the Minx" - have become household names.

I very much hope that both comics will continue to delight boys and girls for another 50 years.

Margaret Thatcher

Mill Hill Station, London, 1939. As children queued up for evacuation to the countryside, where they'd be safe from the German air raids on the big cities, we wouldn't mind betting that lots of them had BEANOS or DANDYS in their haversacks.

DANDY AND BEANO AT WAR

MORE than forty years after it ended, memories of the Second World War are still all too vivid for people who were schoolchildren during those harrowing times . . . memories such as food rationing (even worse, sweet rationing!), Mickey Mouse gas masks, evacuation to the country for city kids, and, of course, DANDY and BEANO.

Although it may seem strange to some that both comics continued to pour out their fun-filled pages during wartime, it's worth remembering that both proved willing and able to add a dash of patriotism to their usual mixture of jokes and japes.

As the clouds gathered over Europe, BEANO and DANDY saw their part in the war effort as being to brighten up the lives of their millions of readers who just lived for the days that their favourite comic dropped through the letterbox. Wartime scarcities, however, meant that both comics were reduced to only twelve pages on alternate weeks.

As for the German leader, Hitler, he found himself facing not only the might of the British and Allied forces but also famous characters like **Desperate Dan** and **Lord Snooty** — all doing their best to put one over the enemy.

As far as is known, Hitler and Goering, the head of the German airforce, were NOT subscribers to DANDY and BEANO during the wartime period, which is a pity really since they appeared regularly in cartoon form in their pages — always of course as the butt of jokes. As far as readers were concerned, the crueller the better!

Aside from the comic strips, both comics went all out to help the war effort, urging their readers to do their own little bit to back Britain. As you can see from the cuttings on this page "Save Paper" was the cry. The reply from loyal readers everywhere was an almost universal "You can count on us — as long as nobody touches our BEANOS and DANDYS"!

By 1945, the war had, of course, come to an end, Hitler having proved no match for the Allied forces — or for **Desperate Dan** — and that was just as well, particularly for the comic staffs of those days.

Just consider this. As the RAF fought off the German airforce in the late summer of 1940, the staffs of BEANO and DANDY continued unabashed to make fun of the enemies at the gate, ignoring to a man the fate that might have lain in store for them if the enemy had successfully invaded!

For a taste of DANDY and BEANO'S unique wartime brand of fun, cast a patriotic glance at the strips on the next few pages . . .

This is one way of changing waste-paper into war weapons, boys and girls.
agic
YOUR
your
rest
know
GR-R
HELPS TO
HUN ON THE RUN!
OME ON CHAPS!
THE NAPPER.
LITTLE SCRAPS,
ER SCRAPPER"!
YOU
CAN HELP BRITAIN
BY COLLECTING
WASTE-PAPER
IF HITLER HAD A MAGIC TELESCOPE WOULD HE SEE THIS?
HIMMEL! DER PIG-DOG BRITISH ARE SAVING ALL THEIR WASTE PAPER
IT'S UP TO YOU!
SPEED OLD HITLER TO HIS GRAVE WITH ALL THE PAPER YOU CAN SAVE!
A K.O. BLOW FOR HITLER!
EVERY British boy would like to biff Hitler good and hard. And every British boy can do it— BY SAVING PAPER. Paper is needed to make munitions, so save up your old papers and magazines and hand them in to the nearest waste paper depot.

CAN YOU BOYS PLEASE TELL ME THE WAY TO THE LOCAL AERODROME?
BOW
WHY, CERTAINLY, SIR! JUST STRAIGHT ALONG THE ROAD!
HUH! OUR PLUS-FOURS ARE BETTER THAN HIS!
I'LL SAY!
TAKE THAT! I AM DER GERMAN SPY! MANY THANKS FOR TELLING ME WHERE DER AERODROME IS!
OUCH!
CONK
LATER
GOSH! THAT CHAP REALLY WAS A SPY! LOOK,—HE'S PINCHED ONE OF OUR PLANES!
HEY! COME BACK WITH THAT PLANE!
HAR! HAR! SOON DER GREAT GERMAN AIR FORCE WILL BOMB YOUR AERODROME TO BITS, AND I WILL GUIDE THEM!
COME ON, SNOOTY, WE'LL BE LATE FOR SCHOOL!
IN SCHOOL
AND NOW WE HAVE HERE PHOTOS OF SOME OF THE MOST FAMOUS LANDMARKS IN THE WORLD, WHENEVER YOU SEE ONE OF THESE YOU WILL KNOW AT ONCE WHERE YOU ARE!
EIFFEL TOWER, FRANCE
TAJ MAHAL, INDIA
THE LEANING TOWER OF PISA, ITALY
STATUE OF LIBERTY U.S.A.
THESE PHOTOS GIVE ME A BEEZER IDEA TO TRICK THE GERMANS!
SNOOTY AND HIS PALS RETURN TO THE LOCAL AERODROME
MY IDEA, SIR, IS TO COLLECT A LOT OF FAMOUS BUILDINGS FROM ALL OVER THE WORLD AND PLACE THEM IN THIS TOWN, THEN WHEN THE GERMAN BOMBERS COME HERE, THEY WONT KNOW WHERE THEY ARE!
SPLENDID IDEA, LORD SNOOTY!
LOOK! THERE ARE ALL MY PLANES SETTING OFF TO GET THE BUILDINGS YOU ASKED FOR!
THAT'S GREAT! THOSE GERMANS ARE GOING TO GET A REAL FRIGHT WHEN THEY COME OVER!
THE R.A.F. IN SOUTH AFRICA.
TABLE MOUNTAIN
THE R.A.F. IN PARIS.
WHAT A DELIGHTFUL VIEW FROM ZE EIFFEL TOWER!
THE R.A.F. IN INDIA.
HI! COME BACK WITH THE TAJ MAHAL!
THE R.A.F. IN ITALY.
HELP! DA R.A.F. KIDNAPPA MUSSOLINI!
DA HELP-A! DA WOW-A!
THE R.A.F. IN AMERICA
O.K. BOYS! WE'VE GOT THE STATUE OF LIBERTY!
THE R.A.F. IN CHINA.
YOU NO PINCHEE GREAT WALL OF CHINA!
WE'LL BRING IT BACK!
THE GERMAN RAIDERS COME OVER AND SEE SO MANY LANDMARKS THEY WONDER WHERE THEY ARE.
ACH! I MUST BE NEEDING DER NEW PAIR OF SPECTACLES. LOOK! THERE IS CHINA DOWN THERE AND AMERICA JUST ROUND THE CORNER! WE MUST HAVE COME TO THE WRONG PLACE!
HEY! YOU CAN'T BOMB ME—I'M HITLER'S PAL!
THAT'S WHAT YOU THINK!
HOMEWARD BOUND PLANES
AMERICA, AFRICA, ITALY, CHINA, INDIA,—ACH! VOT IS THIS? LET US GO HOME, FRITZ, MINE HEAD IS DIZZY!
MUSSOLINI
TABLE MOUNTAIN
HA! HA! THE GERMANS ARE ALL MIXED UP!
GET OUT OF HERE FOR MAKING DER FOOLS OF US!
WOW!!
THAT WAS A BRILLIANT IDEA OF YOURS, SNOOTY! I HOPE YOU GET A MEDAL FOR IT!
OH BOY! JUST WAIT TILL THAT SPY LANDS!

LORD SNOOTY and his pals from Bunkerton Castle set about the enemy in a big way in a series of zany adventures throughout the war.

Take a look at these two adventures from BEANOS issue dated 7th September 1940 and 21st June 1941.

DANDY AND BEANO AT WAR

AS the war continued, life got tougher and tougher for Hitler and his henchmen, especially in the pages of DANDY and BEANO, where they found themselves battered and bemused by top funsters every week!

Both BEANO and DANDY came up with new comic strips for the wartime years, which starred the top villains of the day, the German leader Hitler and the Italian leader Mussolini, proving that in the comic world at least they were bottom of the heap!

MUSSO

ADDIE AND HERMY

DANDY AND BEANO AT WAR

WE end our wartime section with a **Pansy Potter** strip from BEANO which proved that even girls were more than a match for the Nazis!

German airborne troops in action against Pansy Potter in September, 1940.

Airborne Infantry troops in action against the German army in September, 1944. In both cases, the Germans came off second best!

ONE DOG AND HIS MAN!

Every dog has his day, and every DANDY reader has his dog . . . Black Bob, champion sheepdog, and for decades, one of the brightest stars in British comics.

Danger and excitement have been as much a part of this dog's life as minding the flock and competing in sheepdog trials. Whether at home in Scotland's border country with his master, Andrew Glen, or visiting countries like Mexico, Canada and Argentina, Bob has rounded up almost as many crooks, smugglers and spies over the years as lost lambs.

From his first appearance in the 25th November issue, 1944, until he bowed (or bow-wowed) out on 24th July, 1982, the famous collie was voted "Top Dog" a thousand times over by legions of young DANDY readers.

Some memorable moments from Black Bob's numerous adventures appear overleaf . . .

A grim game of swings for Black
BLACK BOB
THE DANDY WONDER DOG
BLACK BOB, the champion sheepdog, was helping in the training of Jack Grant, the boy who wanted to be a farmer. Jack was living with Bob's master, Andrew Glenn, and he was the nephew of the famous shepherd's boss.
Young Jack
but today he
effort. His
broken down
the rim of
While Andrew Glenn went for more posts, Jack set to work with the sledgehammer. With each blow small stones went showering down the quarry face.
Jack cut through the wire with the big axe. He meant to use part of the old fence as a ladder to reach the sheep!
He heaved at the
loose—but at the
quarry edge
Jack had knocked the new post well in—and now it saved his life by checking his fall! Black Bob dashed round the rim of the quarry to get down to the quarry floor.
It was a daredevil leap. Bob landed on a fence post, his weight making the 'ladder' swing across the cliff face towards a bush. Jack seized it and pulled himself on to a ledge.

CARING . . .

One of the most fondly remembered Black Bob stories featured Blind Billy, an Irish boy who arrived in Scotland for an eye operation. Billy's dark world held many hazards, but Bob was always there to protect him until it was time for the boy's successful treatment.

DARING . . .

The safety of the flock comes first! That's a sheepdog's golden rule, and golden eagles are no friends to sheep or their lambs. More than once Bob tangled with the mighty birds and lived to tell the tale.

SHARING . . .

Bob was always most at home with youngsters, whether they were lambs or children. And having the champion sheepdog as guest of honour made any kids' party a day to remember.

IN his long and successful athletics career, Geoff Capes has pitted his mighty frame against some of the top sportsmen in the world.

We suspect, though, that even Geoff — proud winner of the title "World's Strongest Man" — would have struggled to hold his own against the picture-strip strongmen who battled their way through the early days of BEANO and DANDY.

Jak the Dragon-Killer, Strang the Terrible and **Morgyn the Mighty** were just three of the heroic fighters who faced, without flinching, a succession of villains, pterodactyls, massive apes — in fact, monsters of every description — and overcame the lot!

THE STRONGEST MEN IN THE WORLD

JAK THE DRAGON-KILLER

MORGYN THE MIGHTY

STRANG THE TERRIBLE

CHRISTMAS WOULDN'T BE THE SAME WITHOUT THEM!

WHEN Mums and Dads try to slip DANDY and BEANO annuals into their kids' stockings on Christmas Eve, they sometimes have a little trouble making them fit. But if the books aren't there the next morning, those same parents are in BIG trouble! For hundreds of thousands of children now reckon that BEANO and DANDY annuals are as much a part of Christmas as the holly and the ivy, and the fairy at the top of the Christmas tree.

But every tradition has its beginning, and this particular Christmas tale starts in 1938 . . .

FIFTY NOT OUT!

That's right, folks! The DANDY annual 1987 is the 50th book in the series. And pictured below is the one that started it all — the very first DANDY BOOK published way back in 1938.

It was described as a "Monster Comic" then, and cost two and sixpence (for our younger readers, that's less than 13 pence). When DANDY fans picked up this chunky book they must have thought that "Monster" referred to the bargain they'd just received.

Although characters such as Archie The Ape and Helpful Henry who appeared in that annual are now forgotten, this was also the first time between hard covers for Desperate Dan and Korky The Cat. And as we all know, those two comic superstars are alive and kicking in book number 50!

A MENACE'S HANDBOOK

1955 was the first year that mini-menaces the length and breadth of Britain were treated to an annual all to themselves, featuring that master of menacing — Dennis The Menace!

This BEANO star's annuals are now a big hit with comic fans everywhere.

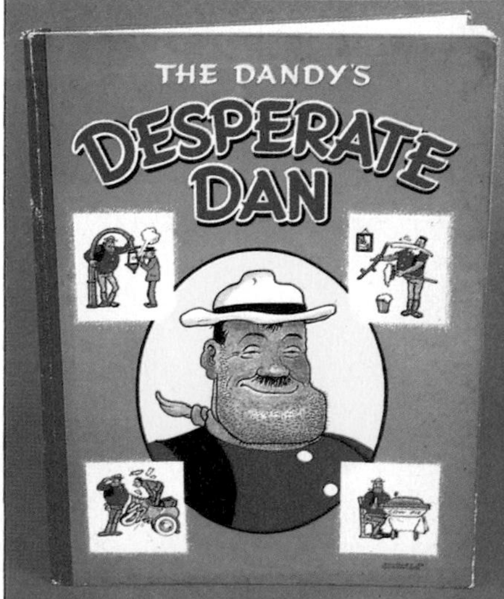

THE BIGGEST NAME IN COMICS

Not to mention the biggest chin, biggest biceps and biggest boots! Needless to say, it was only a matter of time before Desperate Dan grabbed an annual all to himself. The year was 1953.

THIS BOOK HAS CLASS . . .

. . . and that class is every BEANO reader's favourite school class — The Bash Street Kids. Despite their great appeal (to everyone but their long-suffering teacher) it was Christmas 1979 before their own annual appeared.

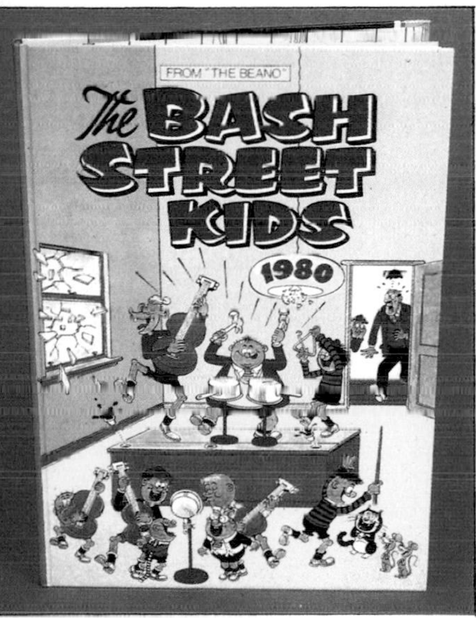

TOP DOG!

It's not often that another comic character "puts one over" on Desperate Dan, but that's exactly what Black Bob did in 1949, when the collie became the first DANDY star to have an annual of his own. Bob went on to feature in another seven annuals during the 1950's and 60's.

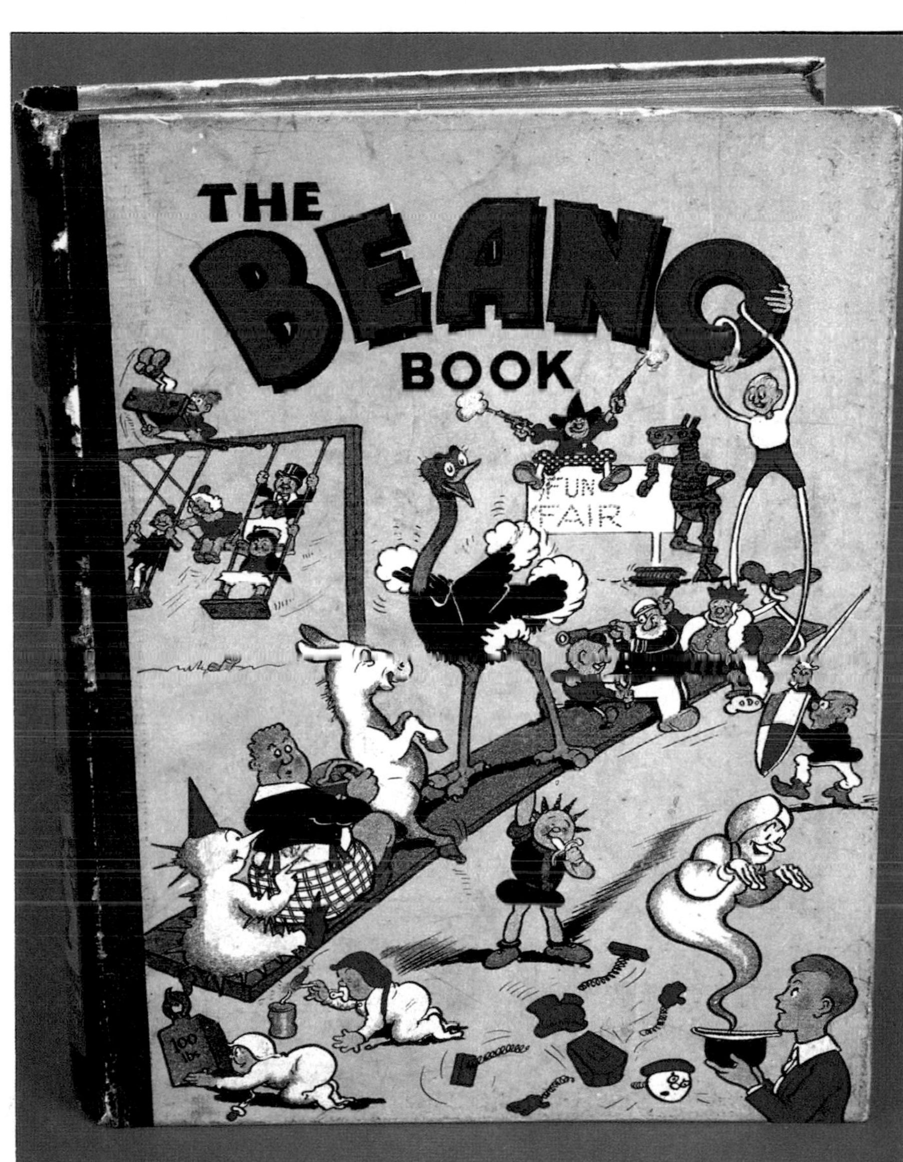

FIRST OF MANY

The BEANO annual's debut in 1939 may have been a year later than DANDY'S, but this particular publication has rarely come second since. The first BEANO BOOK, seen above, began an amazing success story, with sales each year that would be the envy of many famous authors.

That first annual saw the now legendary, Lord Snooty, sandwiched between Hicky The Hare and Brave Captain Kipper, proving that some comic characters stand the test of time better than others.

But every story had its followers, and as if the laughs and thrills provided by those early tales wasn't reward enough, any far-sighted reader who kept their copy in good condition, will be delighted to know that the first BEANO annual is worth more than £100 today.

STARQUOTE
TRY A JOHN CLEESE SILLY WALK, THEY SAID. NO PROBLEM!
DANDY AND BEANO ARE FOR ME THE ONLY TWO TRUSTWORTHY JOURNALS IN THE UNITED KINGDOM.
IF YOU THINK THAT TAKES SOME BELIEVING, HAVE A LOOK AT THE RIPPING YARNS STARTING ON THE NEXT PAGE.
Seriously though, many thanks to one of the world's top comedians for his kind words about two of the world's top comics.

Ripping Yarns

When DANDY and BEANO burst on to the scene in the late thirties, they were joining a wide range of highly popular adventure papers on newsagents' counters.

Weeklies like SKIPPER, ADVENTURE, WIZARD, HOTSPUR and ROVER told their thrilling tales in words, with only the occasional illustration, so it was no surprise that many of the pages in the early years of BEANO and DANDY followed this format.

Although the arrival of TV resulted in young readers demanding a more visual approach from comics, the swashbuckling type stories didn't immediately disappear, but became instead picture strips.

The BEANO went 'all comic' after GENERAL JUMBO made his last appearance on 11th October 1975, but the exploits of BLACK BOB, the Scottish sheepdog, continued to appear in The DANDY until the early eighties, and even today, The Dandy Book continues this tradition by including an adventure story each year.

Tom Captures the Red Robber of the Forests!

THE ADVENTURES OF TOM THUMB

Onions for the King! Tom Thumb's Xmas adventure.

TOM THUMB THE BRAVE LITTLE ONE

A CIRCUS, a shipwreck, a battle for survival on a remote South Seas island — they're the ingredients great adventure stories are made of, and on one famous occasion they were all ingredients in the same BEANO story . . .

SHIPWRECKED CIRCUS

Many a time, Trixie the tightrope walker, Danny the acrobat, Gloopy the dwarf and Horace the educated ape, found themselves in deep trouble or deadly danger, but Samson the circus strongman could always be relied on to lend a large, powerful helping hand.

The Fight against the Monsters from the Sea!

THE SHIPWRECKED CIRCUS

Gloopy is in danger! His only hope is to cycle along a harpoon rope!

BEFORE AND AFTER...

TOM THUMB was one of the first characters to entertain BEANO readers when his adventures appeared as type stories in the comic's early issues. His later exploits, during the 1940's, were in picture strips, and the contrast between these two styles of story-telling can be seen on the left.

The DANDY'S champion sheepdog, Black Bob, also made his first appearance in a type story, before becoming familiar to generations of young readers in numerous picture strip serials.

GENERAL JUMBO

YOUNG **Jumbo Johnson** became an instant general when he climbed into Professor Carter's garden to retrieve his ball.

He came face to face with the miniature armed forces that the Professor had invented and very soon Jumbo was the world's youngest commander-in-chief.

General Jumbo as BEANO readers saw him for the first time on 19th September, 1953. **Jumbo** was to appear off and on in the comic for the next 22 years.

The adventure overleaf is from the Christmas 1953 issue.

GENERAL JUMBO

1 — Young Jumbo Johnson was feeling on top of the world. It was Christmas Eve, AND there was snow on the ground! He liked Christmas for the same reason as everybody else; but he liked snow for a very special reason — the boy General could put his platoon of ski-troops through their paces. The troops were models, of course, only a few inches high, but perfect in every detail. They were radio-controlled by the wonderful gadget on Jumbo's left wrist, and at that moment our cheery chum was testing his ski-troops in a quiet street in Dinchester. Suddenly, a big limousine glided past and Jumbo yelled as a wheel skidded and sent a shower of snow into his face.

2 — Jumbo glared after the big car. It was being driven by a uniformed chauffeur and in the back sat a young boy in posh clothes. The boy General shook his fist at the car. "Algy Ridgeway-Smith!" he muttered. "Young snob!" Algy was the son of B.J. Ridgeway-Smith, the motor millionaire, and he was home for Christmas holidays from his public school in the Midlands. Then Jumbo saw the car draw into the side of the road some distance ahead. Two men had signalled the car to stop. They were both dressed as Santa Claus and had a big barrel of surprise parcels to sell as Christmas gifts. Jumbo saw the chauffeur open the back door of the car and out stepped Algy.

3 — Jumbo pressed a couple of buttons on the control panel. "Step on it, men!" he whispered. "I'm going to give that lad a piece of my mind." Algy was talking haughtily to the Santa Clauses. "I'll take a couple of dozen of your surprise parcels. My chauffeur will pay you," he was saying, when one of the men whipped a sack over his head. At the same time the other man felled the startled chauffeur with a vicious punch to the chin.

4 — Jumbo gaped. The two men were bundling the boy into a horse-sleigh, and in a moment it was gliding swiftly down the street. "Kidnappers!" he gasped. The crooks must have known young Algy planned to go for a drive and had set a trap for him. Luck had favoured the kidnappers. Few people were about. But Jumbo didn't mean to stand and gape for long. He pelted after the sleigh, sending his ski-troops gliding ahead of him.

5 — Faster and faster galloped the sleigh-horse, but Jumbo's little models soon overtook it, with tiny arms and ski-sticks working like quick-fire pistons. Jumbo puffed along behind them. At the right moment he pressed a red button on his control gadget. Immediately the ski-troops turned to fire their pea-shooter rifles at the horse. Ping! Ping! Ping-Ping-Ping!

6 — The tiny missiles did the horse no harm, but they certainly gave it a fright. With a shrill whinny the animal swerved into the side and — CRASH! — the sleigh collided against a lamp standard. "Help! Police!" yelled Jumbo. But the crooks recovered in an instant. One ran up an alley with poor Algy; the other made a grab for General Jumbo.

7 — Jumbo felt himself held in an iron grip. "You're comin' with us, kid," snarled a voice. "And you're goin' where you can't do any more damage with these toys of yours!" After a hurried journey through a maze of alleys, the helpless boys were carried like sacks into a high tenement building. In a fleeting glimpse, Jumbo caught the street name. "Skid Row," he thought. "No. 7 Skid Row." The boys were carried to the attic flat of the tenement and dumped in a damp, ramshackle bedroom.

8 — "Gimme that box o' tricks," snarled one of the kidnappers, tearing the control gadget from Jumbo's wrist. "Good. Now, we're going to squeeze ten thousand pounds ransom outa your dad,toff!" The crooks moved into another room, leaving the door ajar. An ho passed. Suddenly Jumbo sat bolt upright. He passed a pencil and pape to Algy. "Quick," he whispered. "Write an S O S to the police." An then, Jumbo pulled out a model ski-trooper which had been hidd inside his jerkin.

9 — Jumbo tucked the note into the ski soldier's belt. "You can't work the model without the control gadget!" gasped Algy. "Yes, I can," said Jumbo mysteriously. He walked on tip toe to the skylight window. One pane of glass was shattered, allowing Jumbo to stick his head half-through. The boy nodded at what he saw and withdrew his head. Then he placed the ski-soldier on the snow-covered roof and gave the model a shove.

10 — The model went gliding swiftly down the roof. Its tiny skis hit the gutter and bounced the little skier into a leap up and over the street. Jumbo had been careful to point the model in exactly the right direction and it sailed clean through a sky-light window in the roof of the house opposite. Crash! Inside the attic flat, Alf Barker, the coalman, and his wife were having supper when the little skier landed right in Alf's mug of cocoa.

11 — When the Barkers recovered from the shock it was Mrs Barker who spotted the message tucked in the ski-soldier's belt. In a jiffy Alf was jogging along to the nearest police station. And in a few jiffies the police raided the attic at 7 Skid Row. Soon the kidnappers were having a very unhappy Christmas in jail. And Jumbo collected his other ski-troops from the police station where they had been handed in by a passer-by.

12 — Then, later that evening, Jumbo and the Barkers were invited to Algy's luxurious home to celebrate. The Barkers couldn't stay long — they were going to Dinchester Coalmen's Christmas treat — but Algy and Jumbo had a grand time. They were great friends now. Jumbo had brought along some of his model soldiers and soon he had them pulling crackers, carving the turkey and making the Christmas dinner a huge success!

YOU might expect to find a masterpiece like this on the walls of The National Gallery, but in fact, it's a scene from the action-packed story **Eastword Ho With Prince Charlie's Gold,** which appeared as a black and white illustration in the 1955 DANDY book.

THANKS to the magic patch on the seat of his pants, Jimmy Watson could travel back through time, and when it came to spanning decades, Jimmy's adventures did just that, in the pages of The BEANO.
This story appeared in the 24th January and 7th February issues of 1948.

JIMMY AND HIS MAGIC PATCH

1 — Jimmy Watson had been playing his mouth-organ all morning. Jimmy was a good player, but his pal, Dave Thompson, had no ear for music. In desperation Dave loaned Jimmy a book of old legends to keep him quiet. So now Jimmy was deep in the story book. Though he was sitting in the backyard, Jimmy's mind was far away in old Baghdad, for he was reading the story of Ali Baba and the Forty Thieves. "I wouldn't mind joining in the fun there," he murmured.

2 — No sooner said than done! If you're like Jimmy and there's a Magic Patch on the seat of your pants, you must be careful what you say! The Magic Patch had the power to whisk Jimmy back into ancient days, and now before he could say "Turkish delight", Jimmy had whizzed back through time and dropped in on a visit to the Caliph of Baghdad! Still clutching the book, Jimmy landed beside the throne where the Caliph was sitting with his daughter.

3 — A young man was entertaining the Caliph with music while the old boy sat on a cushion, humming away to himself. It didn't take Jimmy two seconds to recognise the young man. It was Ali Baba himself. The Caliph was startled by Jimmy's sudden appearance but before he could summon the guards Jimmy took out his mouth-organ and began to play.

4 — "More!" cried the Caliph as Jimmy finished playing "The White Cliffs of Dover" for the third time. But as Jimmy started off again a great roar came from the gates of the Palace, followed by the clattering of hoofs and the clash of steel. Into the Palace grounds swept a band of forty ragamuffins on horseback. The rascals made short work of the Caliph's bodyguard.

5 — Back to back with the Caliph, Jimmy and Ali Baba put up the best fight they could. But they were unarmed and soon the Caliph was bound to a pillar while Jimmy and Ali Baba lay sprawling on the floor. A big bearded ruffian snatched Jimmy's mouth-organ. "I'll get you for this," gasped Jimmy as the bandits rode off with their loot — and the Caliph's daughter!

6 — When the robbers had gone, Jimmy untied the Caliph. "Cheer up," said Jimmy. "Ali Baba and I will bring your daughter back." "But how will you find the robbers' den?" said the Caliph. Jimmy remembered his book. He snatched it up eagerly and there, sure enough, in the story of Ali Baba was a map showing the way to the cave of the Forty Thieves.

7 — Jimmy and Ali Baba did not waste time explaining their secret to the Caliph. They raced outside to where the camels were tethered. Ali Baba saddled two fast-looking beasts and showed Jimmy how to mount. Then off they set across the desert with Jimmy following the directions in his book. The minarets and domes of Baghdad were soon far behind and cliffs loomed ahead. At last Jimmy told Ali to dismount.

8 — There was no sign of a cave leading into the cliffs and Ali Baba shook his head. But Jimmy was engrossed in the book. "Open Sesame," cried Jimmy, and Ali Baba thought the young English boy had gone off his head with the heat of the sun. "That's the magic pass-word to open the door of the cave," explained Jimmy. Sure enough there was a rumbling noise at the foot of the cliff and a section of the rock opened.

9 — There were two rows of huge earthenware jars lining the sides of the cave but Jimmy and Ali Baba had no eyes for them. For lying at the far end of the cave was a fabulous heap of jewellery, flashing and sparkling in the light. "The robbers' loot!" shouted Jimmy, and they both sprinted up to the pile. There was no sign of the robbers and all thought of danger was forgotten.

10 — With a piece of chalk Jimmy marked out a pitch for marbles. "The robbers haven't returned," he said. "Come on, Ali, I'll play you at marbles." And soon the pair were playing marbles with pearls worth thousands of pounds. Out of the earthenware jars popped the heads of the Forty Thieves, who had been hiding there.

11 — At a signal from their leader the Forty Thieves pounced. An evil-looking robber sent Ali Baba crashing on his face with a wicked kick in the pants and a black-bearded bandit soon had Jimmy by the throat. Jimmy Watson began to wish that his pants hadn't been patched with a piece of magic carpet. "Enough!" cried the leader suddenly. "Spare them — for torture!"

12 — At a signal two of his men went running for a couple of smaller earthenware jars into which Ali and Jimmy were squeezed. "What's the game?" muttered Jimmy. "I don't think their idea of a joke will be the same as mine." It wasn't. Jimmy gulped as the men began to heat up a huge cauldron of oil. "Oh, mother!" gasped Jimmy. "They're going to boil us in oil!"

1 — Jimmy Watson was in a queer fix and no mistake. The Magic Patch on his pants had whisked him back to old Baghdad in the days of Ali Baba and the Forty Thieves. While trying to rescue the Caliph's daughter from the robbers, Jimmy and Ali Baba had been trapped in the robbers' cave. Now the pair of them were jammed tight in two jars waiting to be boiled in oil. But while the robbers sat gloating over the torture to come, Jimmy began to rock his jar slowly to and fro.

2 — Jimmy had been rather upset at the thought of boiling like the Sunday joint, but that had only sharpened his wits. With a thud the jar went over on its side and began to roll straight for one of the marble pillars in the cave. The robbers jerked round in alarm, wondering what the young British boy was doing. Smash! The jar splintered in pieces on the pillar and Jimmy was free. It took him a couple of seconds to recover from his shaking, then he sprang to his feet.

3 — Through the galleries of the cave ran Jimmy with the Forty Thieves hard on his heels, waving their cutlasses and bawling their heads off. As he ran, Jimmy was desperately wondering what to do next and his eyes lit up when he spotted sacks of pearls lying on the floor. Grabbing one of the sacks, Jimmy emptied it on the floor. "This will stop them!" he panted.

4 — The robbers came dashing round the corner to grab Jimmy. Then, swoosh! Their feet went in all directions and, with thuds that shook the cave, they crashed in a heap. As they lay gasping on the floor, Jimmy darted through a nearby doorway. He knew the Caliph's daughter was imprisoned somewhere in the cave and he was determined to free her.

5 — Jimmy wasn't very sure how he would do that as he stumbled along through the darkness, but help was at hand. As Jimmy passed through one of the galleries he heard someone shouting to attract his attention, and running in the direction of the cry he found an old man sitting on a posh-looking carpet in the centre of a cell. Behind him in another cell was the Caliph's daughter.

6 — Feeling in his pocket amongst the marbles, bits of pencil and other odds and ends he carried, Jimmy found exactly what he wanted — a piece of bent wire. The lock was old and rusty and Jimmy found it easy to open with the wire. The old man staggered out and behind him came the rug he'd been sitting on — floating in the air! It was a Magic Carpet!

7 — It took Jimmy some time to get his breath back. "Wait here!" he said to the old chap. "I've got to free the Caliph's daughter!" But the old Wizard had other plans. Nearby were sacks of precious stones, some of the robbers' loot, and the Magic Man began to load this on the carpet, which was still floating in the air. Jimmy chuckled as he tumbled to the idea and gave a hand. Then they both climbed on the carpet.

8 — From the Magic Carpet, Jimmy could see that the robbers were having trouble. Some of them had discovered that the jewels were missing from the cave. They couldn't understand how these jewels and Jimmy had disappeared into thin air. They suspected each other and grumbled until their tempers rose and swords began to clash. "Let's go!" said Jimmy. The Wizard murmured a magic spell and the carpet zoomed down.

9 — It must have been the first air-raid in history. As they swooped down on the robbers Jimmy and the Wizard unloaded the jewels. Bonk! First one robber and then another was cracked on the head and slumped to the ground, out for the count. The dive-bombing was a great success. Soon the attack was over and the Forty Thieves were out of action. Jimmy and his magic pal, however, had lots of work to do.

10 — Jimmy dropped down off the carpet and dashed off to free the Caliph's daughter. When he came running back with her, the Wizard had brought the carpet alongside Ali Baba, who was still in the earthenware jar. With a quick heave, Ali Baba was freed, and now it seemed there was only one thing to do — load up the carpet with the jewels and be off. But Jimmy Watson wanted to even the score with the Forty Thieves.

11 — The cave was stacked with earthenware jars. Jimmy's wheeze was to knock the bottoms out of the jars, and Ali Baba gave him a hand. The robbers were beginning to recover when they were plonked one in each jar in such a way that they could not escape. Soon all the robbers were in the jars and all the jars were roped together while the precious loot was loaded on to the Magic Carpet. What a sight it was as the Forty Thieves started out on the long procession back to Baghdad! Ali Baba and the Caliph's daughter rode on camels, but the Wizard and Jimmy sat on the Magic Carpet. Jimmy had recovered his mouth-organ, which the robbers had stolen, and he kept the robbers going with the tune, "It's a long way to Tipperary!"

UNLUCKY STARS!

LAUGHTER, fun and entertainment are all part of the world of George Cole, Bill Owen and Rolf Harris, but the talented threesome, who have brought lots of enjoyment to millions of TV viewers over the years, actually missed out themselves on a little of childhood's fun — because none of them read BEANO or DANDY!

Maybe that's why, in terms of the comic world at least, they'll always be unlucky stars!

GEORGE (ARTHUR DALEY) COLE

"When you gave birth to BEANO and DANDY, I was an eleven-year-old intellectual who read The HOTSPUR!"

WHERE'S BUTTONS?

HE'S GONE DOWN THE PAPER SHOP FOR MY BEANO.

BILL (COMPO) OWEN

"Whilst I was too old for comics even fifty years ago, my son was a regular reader. However, you do get a plug in my pantomime every year!"

ROLF HARRIS

"I have no memories of either DANDY or BEANO — having never seen a copy in my growing up years in Australia — so sadly I can't chip in with any reminiscenses at all."

Cartoon by Rolf.

THE BEANO has its very own life peer — **Lord Snooty.** He's enjoyed as long a life as the comic, and since His Lordship took his seat in The House Of Laughs in 1938, he's faithfully served King, Queen and millions of BEANO fans.

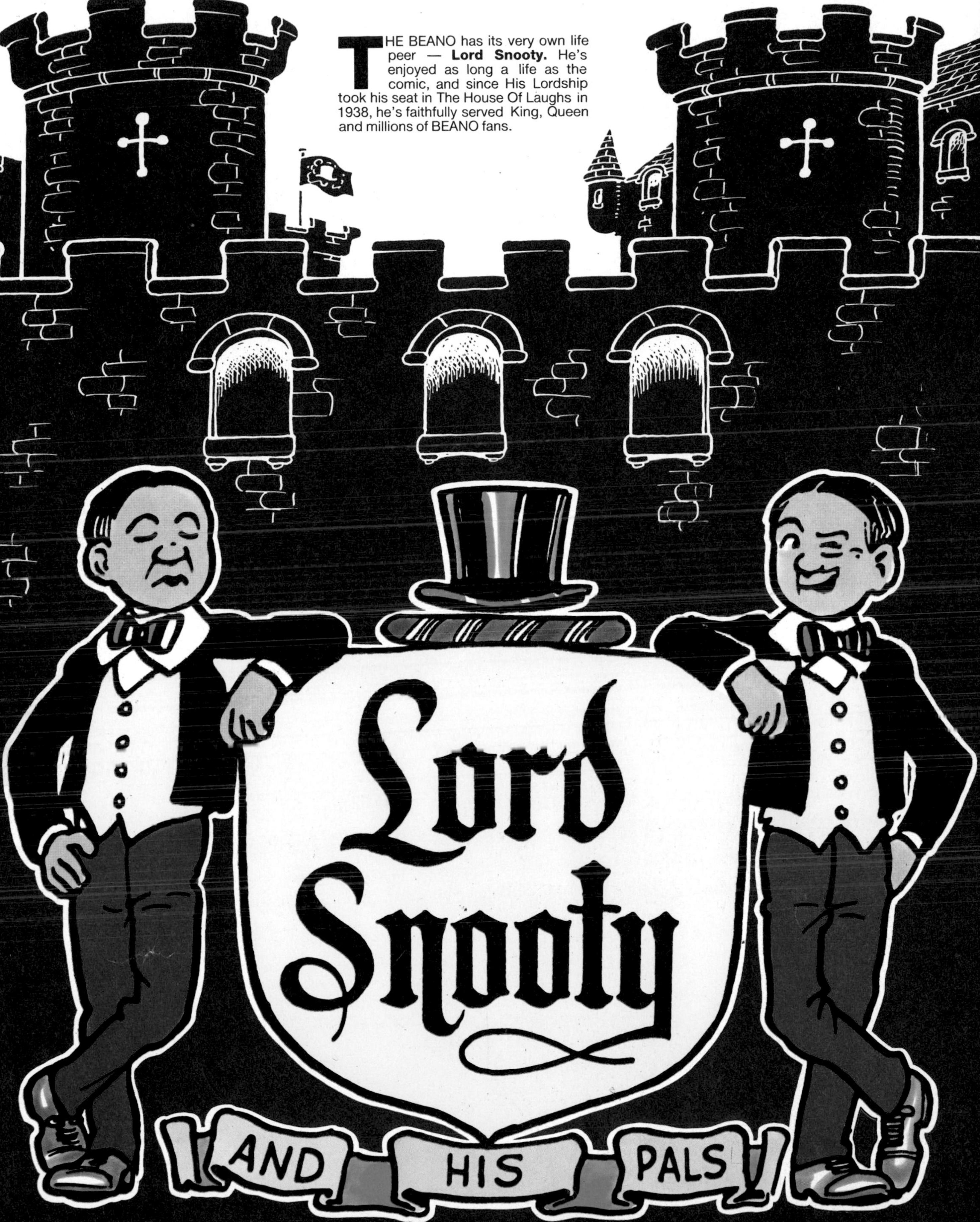

Lord Snooty doesn't go around with his nose in the air — he'd risk standing on a banana skin if he did that — and to prove it, he's invited every reader on a conducted tour of the picture gallery at Bunkerton Castle, his ancestral home.

Way back in his very first story, Lord Snooty abandoned his toffee-nosed companions and befriended this bunch of ragged but loveable scallywags.

But Snooty's original pals didn't last the pace, and his current crew were recruited from other BEANO stories on 30th December, 1950.

There are times when even a member of the nobility has to bow, and that time came for Lord Snooty in 1982, when he encountered a certain prince and princess.

Every lord needs a coat of arms, but when Snooty ordered one for Bunkerton Castle, he discovered there was more than one type of coat of arms.

I'LL CHOP SOME POTATOES FOR CHIPS.
BOO-HOO! OH, THESE ONIONS!
I'LL MAKE SOME REALLY BIG JAM TARTS.
THIS IS A MIXED GRILL.
TREACLE PUDDING
JAM
THUD!
OW! I TOLD JOE YOU DON'T MAKE ROCK CAKES WITH CEMENT!
FLOUR
JAM TART

A question many people ask is, "What does a Lord do when his kitchen staff are on holiday?" Here's the answer!

HELLO! PUT THE SAUCE BACK ON THE TRAIN WHEN YOU'RE FINISHED!
RIGHT, SNOOTY!
IS THAT THE STATION-MASTER? WE CAN'T WAIT FOR THE CUSTARD AND TART TRAIN TO START MOVING!
2nd COURSE DEPOT
CUSTARD
NOW FOR A SECOND HELPING OF POTATOES!
I'LL HAVE MORE BEEF BEFORE THE FIRST COURSE TRAIN MOVES OFF.

Fortunately, Snooty and his pals can enjoy the meal they've prepared without the services of His Lordship's faithful butler, thanks to a large electric train set.

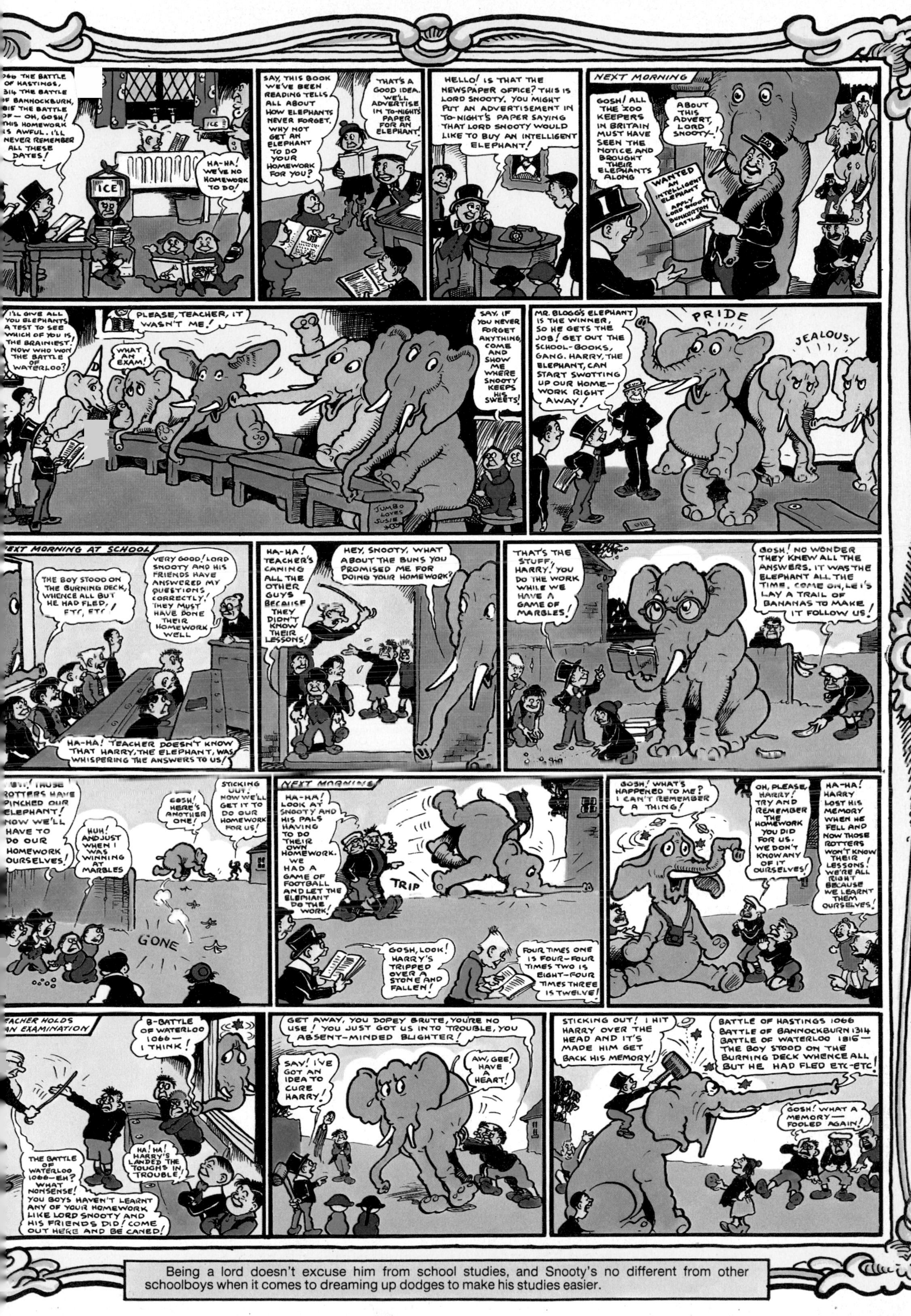

Being a lord doesn't excuse him from school studies, and Snooty's no different from other schoolboys when it comes to dreaming up dodges to make his studies easier.

THE LONG AND THE S

THE DANDY and BEANO can claim the tallest and smallest characters in comic history. Ten foot Danny Longlegs from the DANDY could fit The BEANO'S tiny Tom Thumb into one of his pockets and still have room left for a week's supply of sweets.

Danny had DANDY readers craning their necks when he first walked tall on 17th February 1945, while BEANO readers reached for their magnifying glasses to follow Tom Thumb's adventures from the comic's earliest issues.

The 19th century American celebrity, General Tom Thumb, would have towered over the BEANO character who shares his name. The General was 3 foot 4 inches tall.

The fact that he couldn't reach the slot in a pillar box didn't stop Tom writing letters. Once he'd scrawled a message on a leaf, his very own postal service did the rest . . . air mail, of course.

At only a few inches tall, Tom might have seemed an unusual farmer, but all he needed was the right size of field . . . and a window box proved perfect.

Years before Yuriy Gagarin made his historic space flight, Tom was a high-flier and it only took a firework rocket to make him a mini-astronaut.

Tom loved messing around in boats, sauce boats that is, or any other handy-sized dish he could lay his hands on. And if the bowl came complete with spoons, Tom had a ready-made set of oars.

Being more than twice as tall as his pals didn't stop Danny Longlegs joining in the fun and games. His friends not only went sledging with Danny, sometimes they went sledging ON him.

Danny's extra inches (and feet and yards) meant that there were more close shaves than catastrophes on the sledging slopes . . .

. . . And when he wasn't around to prevent an accident, Danny's long limbs often came to the rescue afterwards.

But Danny was no goody-two-shoes. Those famous legs could also be used for playing tricks at school AND for a quick getaway from an angry teacher.

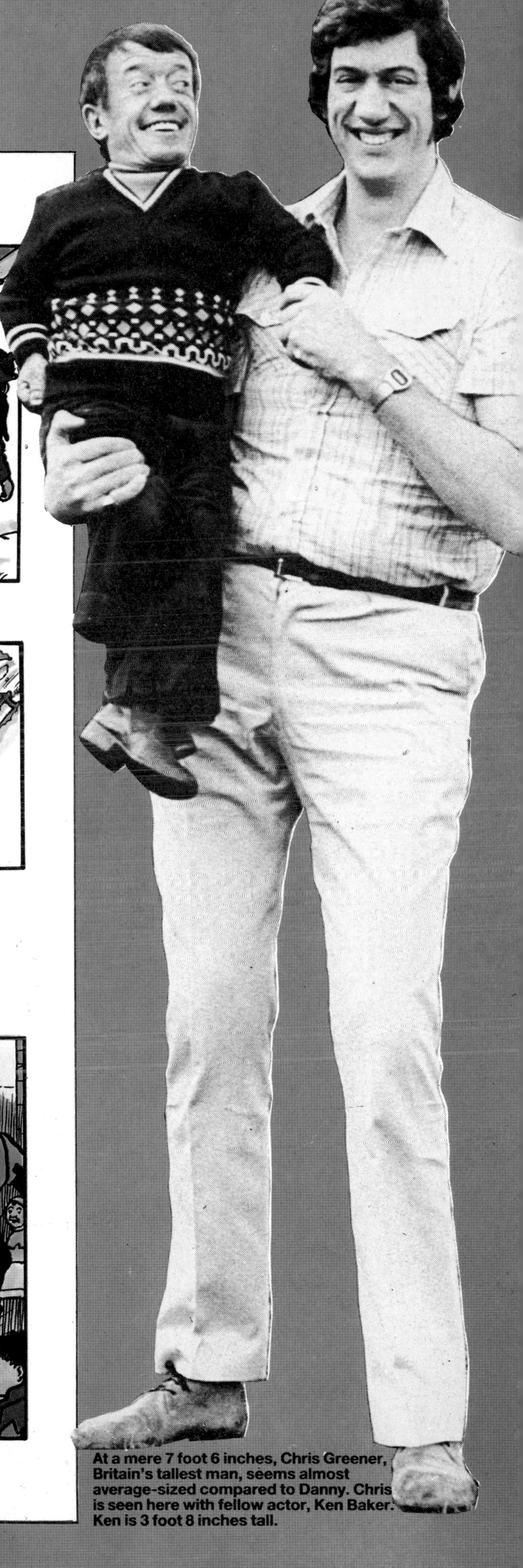

At a mere 7 foot 6 inches, Chris Greener, Britain's tallest man, seems almost average-sized compared to Danny. Chris is seen here with fellow actor, Ken Baker. Ken is 3 foot 8 inches tall.

TWICE THE LAUGHS!

50
GOLDEN YEARS

FOR BEANO and DANDY fans, 1949 was a very good year.

It was only then, four years after the Second World War, that paper shortages came to an end and for readers of the two famous comics, that had one very happy result.

BEANO and DANDY, both of which had been published only every second week since early in the war, could at last resume weekly production — bringing twice as many laughs for their fans!

Here's how BEANO and DANDY announced the great news . . .

Great new stories and thrilling new pictures coming in "The Dandy."

A Famous Old Pal — BLACK BOB

And Two Great New Pals — RABOO and RAJAH

FULL DETAILS IN YOUR NEXT COPY OF "THE DANDY" - GET IT!

On Sale TUES. AUGUST 2ND

HEIGH-HO! HEIGH-HO!
LET EVERYONE KNOW "THE BEANO" IS ON SALE WEEKLY, EVERY FRIDAY NOW.
Make sure of YOUR "Beano" every week by asking your newsagent to keep it for you!

GREAT NEWS
FOR EVERY READER— "THE BEANO" WILL BE ON SALE WEEKLY EVERY FRIDAY
commencing
FRIDAY, 29th JULY.
Make sure of next week's copy of your "Beano" by ordering it at your Newsagent's now!

DON'T FORGET
FRIDAY, 29th JULY
is the day your next copy of "THE BEANO" IS ON SALE. FROM THAT DATE YOU WILL GET YOUR "BEANO"
WEEKLY, EVERY FRIDAY!

A HOLIDAY AT THE GRAND HOTEL! "THAT," THINKS KORKY, "WILL BE SWELL". BUT SOON HE STARTS TO TEAR HIS HAIR, FOR ALL HIS MOUSEY MATES ARE THERE!

Korky the Cat

IF there's one thing kids enjoy almost as much as getting up to mischief themselves, it's reading about somebody else doing it — and maybe that's why that superstar of the cat world, **Korky**, has won so many fans since his first appearance in the very first DANDY.

During one or two of **Korky's** nine lives, he has had a paw in enough ploys, tricks and pranks to fill this book several times over!

As you'll see from the Easter **Korky** we've pulled from the archives, **Korky** is sometimes 'assisted' by his nephews, the **Kits.** In fact, many **Korky** fans have a special soft spot for the adventures which feature the fun-loving mini-Korkies.

Even the **Kits** would agree though, that it's **Korky** who is the star of the show, appearing as the DANDY cover character right up until 17th November, 1984.

But this cat has had his day as cover kit and since 1984, when it took somebody as strong as **Desperate Dan** to push him off the cover, **Korky** has happily indulged in his own particular brand of trickery on the inside pages of the comic — still producing lots of laughs for his fans. Proving he's the comic world's top cat.

We doubt if the other cats on this page would disagree.

KORKY during his younger days, looked very different from the cat you're familiar with today, but he provided just as many laughs. Here's a classic episode from 12th March, 1938.

KLASSIC KORKIES

L OTS of **Korky** fans are especially fond of the adventures which appeared during the classic period of BEANO and DANDY in the fifties — so here for your enjoyment is a selection of classic Korkies, celebrating landmarks in the calendar from New Year to Christmas. Our first, from DANDY issue dated January 2nd, 1954 proves just what a smart cat **Korky** is!

KORKY THE CAT

KORKY'S PALS ARE CRAFTY GUYS,
BUT HE GIVES *THEM* A BIG SURPRISE—
HE WISHES THEM A *GOOD NEW YEAR*
WITH A SNOWBALL SLAP BEHIND THE EAR!

KLASSIC KORKIES

THIS Easter **Korky**, from 12th April, 1952, demonstrates that where **Korky** and his nephews the **Kits** are concerned, one plus three equals more than four times the fun.

KORKY THE CAT

KORKY'S EGGS BOUNCE DOWN THE SLOPE,
THE KITTENS CATCH THEM NEATLY.
AND EVERY KIT FEELS SUCH A DOPE
WHEN THE EGGS START HUMMING SWEETLY!

We end our **Korky** section with an episode from DANDY issue dated 25th December, 1954, showing a happy looking **Korky** coming off best — as he usually does!

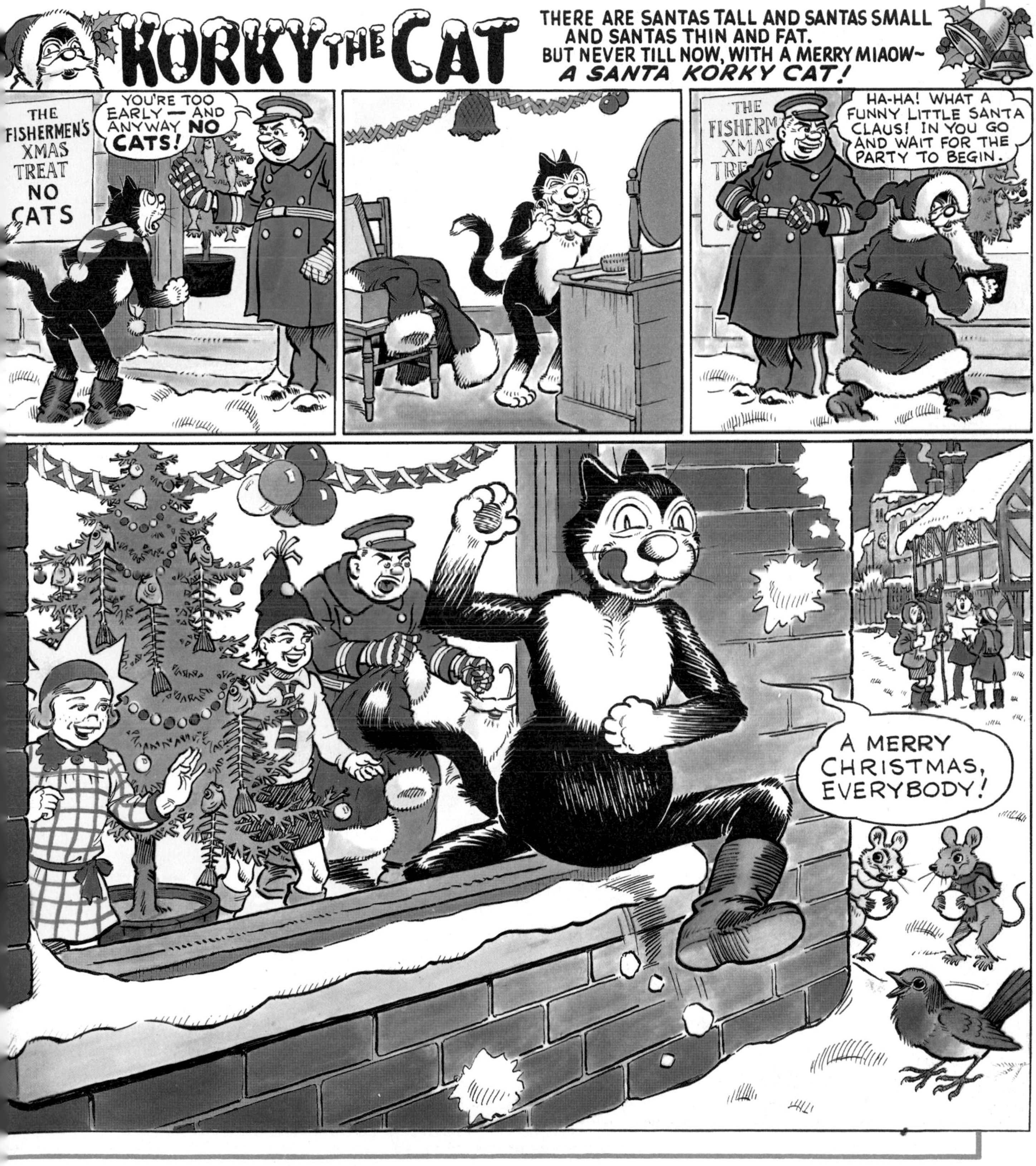

THERE ARE SANTAS TALL AND SANTAS SMALL
AND SANTAS THIN AND FAT.
BUT NEVER TILL NOW, WITH A MERRY MIAOW~
A SANTA KORKY CAT!

A MERRY CHRISTMAS, EVERYBODY!

THE Bash Street Kids
INK

WHAT SUBJECT WOULD YOU LOT LIKE TO DO FOR YOUR SCHOOL PROJECT?
S-I-L-E-N-C
BAH! THEY'RE SO BUSY READING "BEANOS" THEY DIDN'T EVEN HEAR ME!

NOW

YAHOO!
YOU'RE EXPECTING US, I SEE!
"BEANO" EDITOR
THUNDER OF SHOES!
SAND BAGS

RATTLE!
SUCK
MILK
CARDBOARD CUT-OUT
"BABY-FACE" WRITER
"RODGER THE DODGER" WRITER
SNEAKING OUT
"SMUDGE"
"BALL BOY" WRITER
FLIP
"BEANO" EDITOR
THESE ARE THE "BEANO" SCRIPTWRITERS.

THE STORIES CAN BE TOLD...

ONE question seems to have particularly fascinated lots of BEANO and DANDY readers over the years — no, it's not why Dennis always wears a striped jumper or why Dan is always — er — Desperate!

The question readers most often ask is, in fact, a simple one — "How are our favourite comics actually made?"

That's why, in 1983, after wading through lots of letters asking just that question, the editor of BEANO decided to satisfy his readers' curiosity in true comic style with this **Bash Street Kids** episode which appeared on 5th November of that year.

Providing lots of laughs on the way, the strip took readers through the whole process which ends with your favourite comic characters starring in your favourite comics each week.

In real life, of course, putting together BEANO and DANDY isn't as crazy (quite!) as shown here, but take it from us, there are plenty of jokes and japes enjoyed by the staff in both offices, lots of which never appear in the comics!

At the same time, though, it takes lots of work from lots of people to produce your favourite comic.

How much? To get some idea, let's have a look at what happened after this Bash Street Kids episode began life as an idea in a scriptwriter's head.

The scriptwriter first put his idea down on paper something like this . . .

BASH STREET KIDS

Picture 1. Title picture — show artist's hand lettering title.

Picture 2. Picture — Teacher talks to class. Head and shoulders only. Class unseen.
Teacher — "What subject would you lot like to do for your school project?"

Picture 3. Picture — Teacher looks on angrily as class reads Beanos, totally ignoring him.
Teacher — "Bah! They're so busy reading 'Beanos', they didn't even hear me."

. . . and so on.

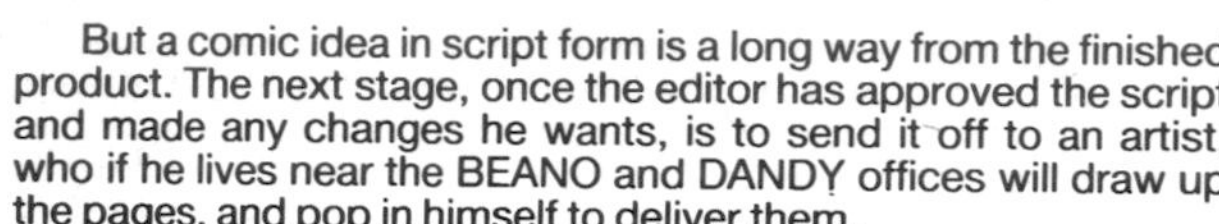

But a comic idea in script form is a long way from the finished product. The next stage, once the editor has approved the script and made any changes he wants, is to send it off to an artist, who if he lives near the BEANO and DANDY offices will draw up the pages, and pop in himself to deliver them.

If, however, artists live some distance away, scripts and artwork often have to be posted back and forward until the editor is completely satisfied with the final job.

What we have now is the artwork, normally drawn at twice the normal size, with no words and no colour, just like the example below — and this is where things start to become more complicated!

At this stage, a print of the page is taken and sent to the BEANO and DANDY colourists department, where skilled artists add colour which you eventually enjoy in the printed comic.

Meanwhile, the words you read in the balloons are set in type. Balloons are drawn carefully around them and then stuck down on the black and white page. The next vital task is carried out by skilled letterers who handletter words which need special emphasis, like the SILENCE in picture three of this script.

Next comes a very important stage as the pages are checked for any mistakes and passed as being ready for publication by the editor.

The ballooned page and colour guide are then sent to the process department to be photographed and plastic plates made, which can then be placed on the massive letterpress printing presses which finally produce the comics.

At this stage too, everybody involved is determined that only perfect BEANOS and DANDYS will reach you, the reader. When they are, a button is pushed and the presses finally roll!

Within an amazingly short period of time, thousands and thousands of BEANOS and DANDYS are printed, all ready to be distributed to eager readers nationwide.

Phew! It's a mindboggling task, isn't it? But producing these two famous comics every week produces some mindboggling statistics too.

For instance, each comic puts together more than 1000 pages each year, which means over 800 scripts and around 11,000 individual pictures!

Our calculator practically blew up as we tried to estimate how many pictures the two comics have produced during their fifty golden years — but we reckon we're not far wrong with a figure of one billion!

MEET THE MENACE!

CALL anyone under the age of fourteen a menace and he or she would probably say, "Thanks for the compliment!"

Ninety-nine kids out of a hundred would just love to be likened to BEANO'S mischievous adult-baiting Dennis the Menace!

Since he first began menacing in the pages of BEANO way back in 1951, Dennis has really struck a chord with kids of all ages, though we suspect lots of adults wish that he hadn't!

As his popularity has grown, the initial half page black and white Dennis strip has been transformed into the front and back covers of the current BEANO.

For the story of Dennis the Menace and a look at some of his top adventures, read on . . .

Here's a real collectors' item — the very first Dennis the Menace strip, originally published in BEANO 17th March, 1951.

STARQUOTE

"Wee Jimmy is based on Dennis the Menace (he's probably the nearest living thing to him!) and of all his possessions, he's most proud of his membership of the Dennis The Menace Fan Club!

When you next see Jimmy on stage or television compare him to Dennis. There are lots of similarities. Both have that likeable cheeky streak in their nature, and when it comes to creating menace and mayhem, there isn't a double-act to compare with Jimmy and Dennis" . . . THE KRANKIES.

1953 was a red-letter year for **Dennis** fans when their favourite comic strip, by now in two colours, was extended to a full page.

Then on **14th April, 1962,** Menaces' lives became even brighter when Dennis was promoted to the back cover of the comic, now in spectacular full colour.

But Dennis knew he had finally made it, on **14th September, 1974** when he menaced Biffo the Bear from the front cover of BEANO.

It hasn't been recorded what Biffo said when he heard the news but if Gnasher was around, we suspect it wasn't a lot.

GOLDEN YEARS
SIREN!
3p
SEP. 14th, 1974.
'MORNING, ALL!
DENNIS'S HOUSE
PC PYE
EXCUSE US, OFFICER!
DENNIS THE MENACE
DOG SHOW
GRAND PRIZES— AND A SPECIAL £5 AWARD FOR THE QUIETEST AND BEST-BEHAVED DOG IN SHOW.
PRETTY TOODLES! NOW I'LL GIVE YOU A NICE BRUSHY-WUSHY!
HEH! HEH! THAT FIVER'S AS GOOD AS MINE!
HMM! I HAVE A PLAN.
GROOMING BRUSHES.
SNIGGER!
ITCHING POWDER
EEK!
SCRATCH!
DENNIS'S DOG
STEADY, PONGO! GOOD BOY!
BAH! ALL THESE DOGS THAT ARE SCRATCHING ARE DISQUALIFIED!
THEN—
AGH! THAT SAVAGE BULLDOG'S BITTEN ME!
BULLDOG
GO—AND NEVER DARKEN OUR SHOW AGAIN!
HEE! HEE! THAT'S ANOTHER RIVAL AWAY THANKS TO DAD'S SPARE SET OF FALSE TEETH!
NOW TO DEAL WITH THE OTHERS.
MEAT PASTE
RUBBER BALL
ARF!
YELP!
YAP!
YIP! YIP!
BOW! WOW!
HOWL!
BOUNCE
YOUR NICE, QUIET, OBEDIENT DOG WINS ALL THE PRIZES, LAD!
FIRST
GOOD! LET'S HAVE THAT FIVER!
ALL THESE BADLY BEHAVED BRUTES ARE DISQUALIFIED!
SUDDENLY—
THERE HE ITH! THATH THE WOTTER WHO PINCHED MY PONGO!
SNATCH!
WHAT? D'YOU MEAN TO SAY HE WAS FOOLING US WITH A TOY DOG?
JUDGE
HUH!
YELP!
AFTER HIM!
HELP! CALL 'EM OFF!
ARF!
YOWOO!
1962

Enter Gnasher, the kind of dog — mean and moody — who is bound to be a boy's best friend. This episode from BEANO 31st August, 1968, shows the menace of the dog world meeting the menace of the human world for the very first time.

They were an instant hit together (and with BEANO fans too!) By 1977, **Gnasher** was so popular that he was given his own page in the comic.

Better known than any Crufts winner, there was a national outcry when **Gnasher** 'went missing' in 1986. Luckily for fans everywhere, the two menaces were happily re-united.

5th May, 1979, and comic fans who'd always thought the best place for bacon is on the breakfast table, suddenly discovered a pig who was a hero.

His name was, of course, **Rasher**, Dennis's new pet, who was to add swill power to the menace's will power from then on.

By 1984, **Rasher** also had his own comic strip in BEANO. Breakfast would never be the same again!

SIMPLY NOT CRICKET

It's the match cricket fans have always wanted — Dennis's team versus Walter's. But poor old Walter discovers that cricket's no game for softies!

WALTER – PRINCE OF SOFTIES

SOFTIES of the world, take heart — because Walter, Prince amongst softies, is a star!

Walter, at the wrong end of a succession of menaces in countless issues of BEANO, has become a great favourite with Dennis fans everywhere.

But Walter is not your average comic strip 'hero'. He's such a 'scaredy', for instance, that we suspect he'd never read a Dennis story himself because he'd be too frightened!

He's the kind of boy too who'd never go butterfly collecting in case the butterflies turned nasty!

But softy or not, as the examples on this page show, Walter can sometimes turn the tables on Dennis.

However often he's menaced, Walter, with his faithful hound Foo Foo, is determined to prove that one day softyism will rule. Okay?

No prizes for guessing who told the park-keeper that Dennis had broken one of his flowers!

Watch out, Walter — you're about to be menaced!

OUCH! Dennis gets a painful shock when Walter suddenly becomes an expert in soft defence!

MEET KENNETH THE MENNETH

COMEDIAN Ken Dodd enjoys the world of laughter — as a performer and a fan.

Over the years, Ken has won himself a reputation as a top comedian, bringing smiles to the faces of his legions of fans with his sparkling performances on stage and TV.

But when Ken's not enjoying the glare of publicity, he still likes to stay immersed in the world of top class humour — sitting back for a quiet chuckle, reading BEANO and DANDY!

In fact, Ken is so tickled by the two comics that he even appeared in a TV show once as **Kenneth the Menneth!**

STARQUOTE

"My love of comics goes way back. The day The BEANO appeared through my letterbox was fun day, and reading The BEANO helped to lay the foundation of my sense of humour. In fact, I still read The BEANO. Lord Snooty and The DANDY'S Desperate Dan are among my favourite comic characters.

One of the greatest honours of my TV career was when I was given permission to dress up as Dennis the Menace for a TV show!"

Seeing is believing when you meet The DANDY'S . .

CURIOUS CREATURES

YOU won't find a *Pobble* or a *Grockle* in any zoo or wildlife park, but for years, DANDY readers knew exactly where these bizarre beasts could be found . . . in the pages of their favourite comic.

There were a lot of new faces in The DANDY's first issue, but none had stranger features than Jimmy Johnson's Grockle.

It all started when Jimmy's uncle sent his nephew a giant egg from South America. When it hatched, out popped Grockle, a creature that looked like a dragon's second cousin.

Pobble didn't make an appearance until 26th January, 1952, when young Willie Willikins saw a space craft crash to Earth. The schoolboy was startled when Pobble stepped out of the grounded craft, but imagine his amazement when the alien creature picked him up and rubbed noses with him.

Pobble is seen here pitting his wits against a more familiar animal — an angry bull.

A KORKER OF A CORONATION!
KORKY THE CAT
"KORKY CAT, KORKY CAT, WHERE HAVE YOU BEEN?"
"I'VE BEEN TO LONDON TO SEE THE QUEEN."
"KORKY CAT, KORKY CAT, WHAT DID YOU THERE?"
"I CHEERED HER AND CHEERED HER FROM UP IN THE AIR."
I KNOW HOW I CAN SEE THE CORONATION PROCESSION.

JUNE 2nd 1953 and the nation unites in celebration of the coronation of Her Majesty Queen Elizabeth the Second.

In London, crowds throng the streets, hoping to catch a glimpse of the new monarch.

Some are doubly lucky, spotting another national figure doing his own little bit to make the celebrations complete.

His name — **Korky the Cat!**

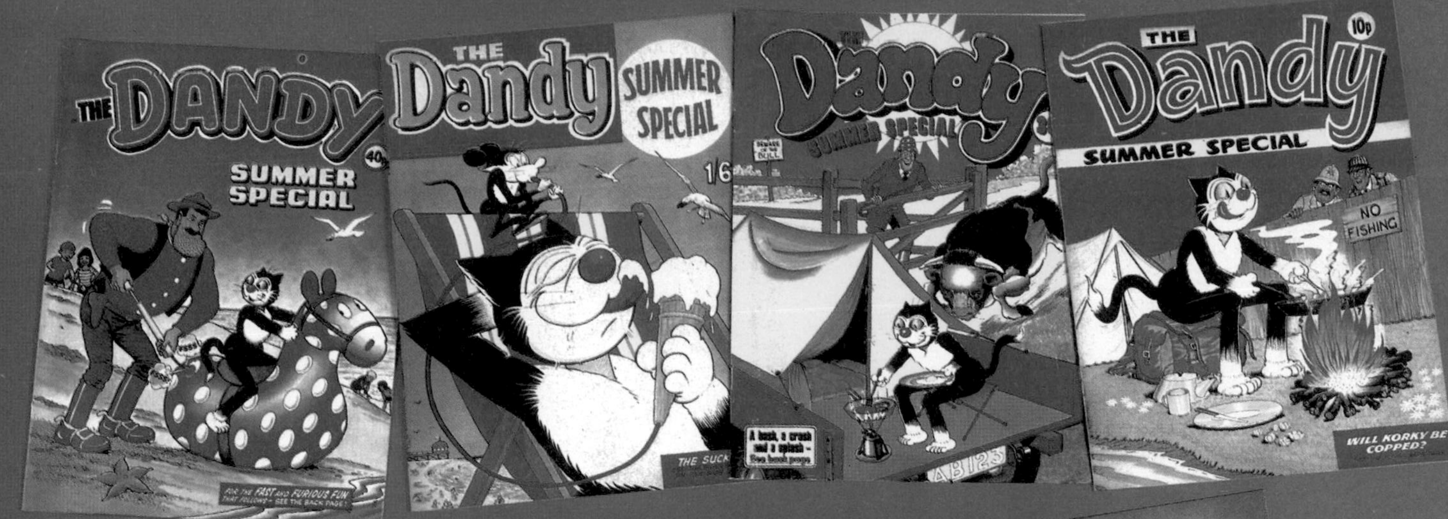

MAKING SUMMER SPECIAL!

AS you might expect, lots of BEANO fans fall about laughing when they read DANDY, while at the same time lots of DANDY fans have a great hoot whenever they pick up BEANO.

Even so, in all the years the two famous comics have been on the news-stands, only once have their readers been able to buy a combined BEANO-DANDY publication.

That big moment came in 1963 with the issue of the DANDY-BEANO Summer Special — a landmark in publishing history and an immediate big seller.

In the very next year, summer became even brighter for comic fans everywhere as both BEANO and DANDY began publishing their own Summer Specials, a tradition which has continued right up to the present day, these colourful publications with their big, fun-packed pages making summer very special indeed!

SALT and pepper, Laurel and Hardy . . . BEANO and DANDY. The comics' names have been linked so often over the years that it's now difficult to think of them individually, but there is one thing that separates the two. The DANDY is definitely the NOISIEST comic in Britain.

In fact, it's the comic that likes to say . . .

Here they are . . . The DANDY'S greatest hits . . . and bangs, prangs, thumps and whumps, that mean more ear-splitting yells per page than any other comic.
YEOW!
PRANG
YOW-EEK!
SWING!
WHUMP!
OUCH!
YAHOO!
AARGH!

YAHOO!

YEOW!

CRASH!

BIFF! BIFF!

OOYAH!

OUCH!

OOYAH!

HELP!

AARGH!

APRIL FOOLERY

A BIG fun landmark each year for all BEANO and DANDY fans is, of course, April 1st.

That's when readers all over the country take to April Fooling their pals with the kind of tricks and japes Dennis the Menace would be proud of.

Not surprisingly, BEANO and DANDY enjoy getting in on the act too. Over the years, both comics have come up with some sparkling April spoofs and comic strips of their own.

Most readers would agree that April Foolery BEANO and DANDY style is hard to beat!

This clever April spoof appeared in DANDY issue dated 4th April, 1964.

MY HOME TOWN **Huntingbury**

A DANDY PRIZE FOR EVERY READER WHOSE ENTRY IS FEATURED ON THIS PAGE.

HUNTINGBURY, in the South Riding of Yorkshire, dates back to the time of the Ancient Britons, who had a fortress here called Loof Lirpa. It was the only fortress to resist the Roman Legions. For centuries, no explanation of this remarkable achievement could be found, but old manuscripts, discovered and translated in 1957, revealed that the fortress was built in four sections mounted on wheels. During the night, the besieged Britons would dismantle their fortress and wheel it quietly away to a new position, leaving the Roman soldiers baffled time and again.

Fried frog is a Huntingbury delicacy. During the Napoleonic Wars, feeling against the French ran so high that, in 1811, the Town Council decreed that all frogs found within the town walls should be caught and fried. The townspeople quickly developed a liking for this French dish, and since that time an annual Frog Feast has been held. In recent years, owing to a frog shortage, chocolate frogs have been eaten instead.

In the centre of Huntingbury is a huge crater now filled with water. This was the site of Huntingbury Hall, where the wicked Squire Pitt blew himself to bits. The story goes that on November 5th, 1561, the squire confiscated all the fireworks in the town, and hid them in his cellar. But the townsfolk weren't done out of their Guy Fawkes Night. A carelessly-discarded cigarette-end set off the hidden fireworks. Neither the Hall nor the squire was ever seen again!

This quaint bridge was really intended to be a ship! In the yard where the ship was built, a mistake was made in the measurements, and nobody noticed that the ship was twice as long as it was meant to be. When launched, the vessel stuck fast between the two banks of the river. Rather than break it up, a hole was broken in its sides to let the river run through, and the ship became a bridge.

The team was taken to be a Scottish one, especially when the players took the field in tartan kilts. The Wanderers went on to win the Scottish Cup, the only English team ever to do so.

Billy Whizz found that April 1st wasn't much fun at all in this BEANO adventure from 1978.

DID JONAH SINK THE TITANIC?

WHEN that mighty liner "The Titanic" went down in April, 1912, icebergs were blamed for the terrible disaster.

What we ask you to consider now is that there may have been an even more terrible cause of the catastrophe — by the name of Jonah!

Our case rests upon Jonah's long career of mayhem and destruction on the high seas, a career during which the sea-goon so often sunk the unsinkable that even the most able-bodied seaman could be reduced to a gibbering wreck at the mere mention of his name.

As for comic fans, they were often reduced to helpless laughter during the five years the world's most useless sailor starred in the pages of BEANO.

But could Jonah have sunk the Titanic? Read the tales overleaf and come to your own conclusion . . .

"Titanic" heads for a watery grave . . .

The "S.S. Indian Club" goes down . . .

The "Pride of Berlin" goes down . . .

Half the British Merchant Navy goes down . . .

JONAH

A BRAND-NEW CARGO SHIP, THE S.S. "MINERVA," IS LEAVING THE GREEK PORT OF ATHENS — BOUND FOR BRITAIN —
S.S. MINERVA
S.S. MINERVA

— ABOARD IS THE WEALTHY OWNER, FRED ARISTOTLE — BOUND FOR A GOOD DUCKING IN THE MEDITERRANEAN —

— WHILE IN HER HOLD, LIES A MASSIVE BLOCK OF MARBLE FOR SHIPMENT TO HULL — BUT BOUND FOR THE BOTTOM OF THE SEA!
I. CHIPP, SCULPTOR, HULL.

THE REASON FOR THESE IMPENDING DISASTERS LIES IN THIS INNOCENT-LOOKING CRATE —

SCUFFLE
SCRATCH
SCRAPE
TORTOISES

— NO! NOT THE TORTOISES — BUT THE NAUTICAL NIT-WIT WHO CRAWLED UNDERNEATH 'EM ON THE DOCK-SIDE AT ATHENS!
HO-HO! WE'RE AT SEA, MATES! THANKS FOR HIDING ME!

ALL I'VE GOT TO DO NOW, IS TO AMUSE MYSELF DOWN HERE UNTIL WE'RE TOO FAR OUT AT SEA FOR THEM TO PUT ME ASHORE AGAIN.

I. CHIPP, SCULPTOR, HULL.
AH! A BLOCK OF MARBLE.
I COULD TRY MY HAND AT SCULPTURIN'.

I'LL CARVE A STATUE OF MYSELF. THEY MIGHT PUT IT IN THE BRITISH MUSEUM.

AND SO, TO WORK —
NOT A BAD LIKENESS, EVEN ALTHOUGH I SAY IT MYSELF!

MEANWHILE, ON THE BRIDGE....
WELL, YOU CAN BE QUITE CERTAIN OF ONE THING, CAP'N! JONAH ISN'T ABOARD! I MADE A THOROUGH SEARCH.

GOOD WORK, CHARLIE!

HALF A DAY LATER
FINISHED AT LAST— AGGH!
SWAY
NO!
JONAH REX
THE BASE IS TOO SMALL, AND AS THE SHIP ROLLS —

SUFFERIN' SEA-SLUGS! RIGHT THROUGH THE HULL!
CRASH!
REX

HELP!
WHAT A TRAGEDY! MY STATUE WAS A WORK OF ART!

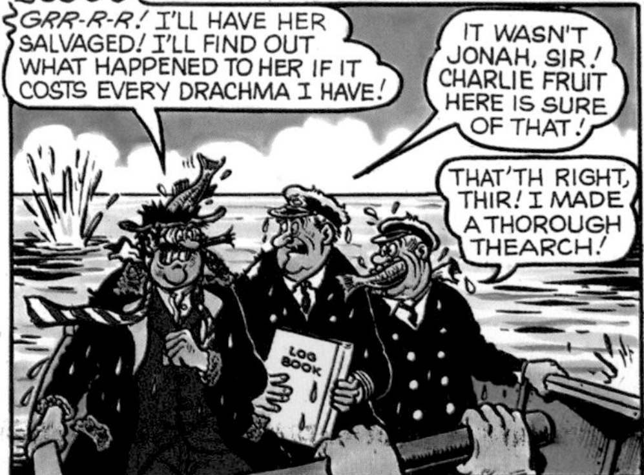
GRR-R-R! I'LL HAVE HER SALVAGED! I'LL FIND OUT WHAT HAPPENED TO HER IF IT COSTS EVERY DRACHMA I HAVE!
IT WASN'T JONAH, SIR! CHARLIE FRUIT HERE IS SURE OF THAT!
THAT'TH RIGHT, THIR! I MADE A THOROUGH THEARCH!
LOG BOOK

AND SO, AT GREAT EXPENSE, THE S.S. "MINERVA" IS RAISED FROM THE DEPTHS.

HERE SHE COMES! THE DIVERS HAVE RIVETTED A METAL PATCH OVER THE PLACE WHERE SHE WAS HOLED AND NOW THEY'RE RAISING HER WITH COMPRESSED AIR!
HOO-OO!
HISS-SS
S.S. MINERVA
WELL! I STILL SAY IT WASN'T JONAH, CAP'N!

YES, SIR! I CAN ALWAYS RELY ON CHARLIE TO — ERK!
S.S. MINERVA
THE PATCH!
IT WAS 'IM!

SO! YOU MADE A THOROUGH SEARCH, DID YOU, FRUIT? WELL, IN A FEW MINUTES THEY'LL BE MAKING A THOROUGH SEARCH FOR YOU, FOOL — A FRUITLESS ONE!
NO!

THE Jonah adventure on the left, from BEANO, issue dated 12th November, 1960, featured the most horrible piece of sculpture ever shaped by man and the only one ever to sink a ship — all thanks to you know who!

Three years and lots of sunken ships later, on 8th June, 1963, **Jonah** made his last appearance in BEANO. Not surprisingly, he found himself up to his neck in raging water!

THE Dandy
3D
EVERY TUESDAY
No. 1000—JAN. 21st, 1961.
KORKY the CAT
THIS IS MY THOUSANDTH BIRTHDAY, BOYS. I'VE APPEARED IN 1000 ISSUES OF THE "DANDY." I'M GOING OFF TO GET MY PRESENT FROM THE EDITOR.
WE'LL HAVE TO GIVE KORKY A PRESENT, TOO.
I'VE GOT AN IDEA.
WAREHOUSE
HERE ARE TWO IN THE WOODPILE.
WAREHOUSE
WE GOT PLENTY IN THERE.
KORKY
WE'LL POP HIS PRESENT THROUGH THE LETTER BOX.
HAPPY BIRTHDAY, KORKY. THERE'S A THOUSAND MICE TO KEEP YOU COMPANY.

GREAT MOMENTS IN HISTORY

50
GOLDEN YEARS

HANDS up anybody who can remember the date of the **American Declaration of Independence** or the **Battle of Trafalgar.**

Tough, isn't it? But here's one great moment in history we're sure nobody will ever forget. It came in 1961 when BEANO and DANDY both published their **1000th issue!**

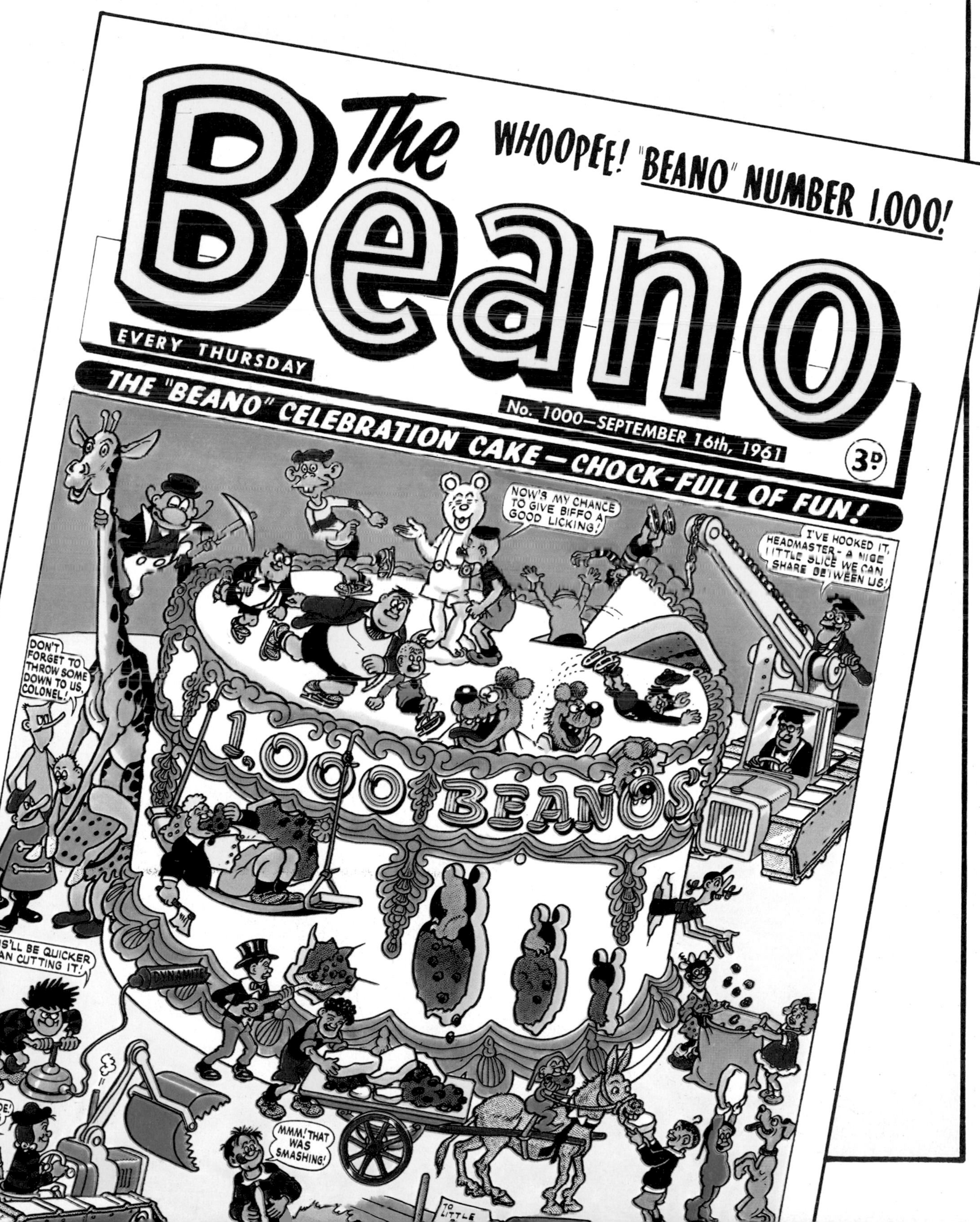

The Beano
3D
EVERY THURSDAY
No. 1256—AUG. 13th, 1966.

BIFFO THE BEAR
ANOTHER ADVENTURE WITH BOATING BIFFO.
HM! LOOKS LIKE ROUGH WEATHER AHEAD!
STORM APPROACHING! ALL HANDS ON DECK TO BATTEN DOWN THE HATCHES!
STEADY AS SHE GOES! MIND THAT BIG WAVE!

SPLOOSH!

MAYDAY! S.O.S! WE'RE GOING DOWN BY THE BOWS!

LOOKS LIKE THIS IS THE END OF BIFFO'S BOAT, READERS!
ABANDON SHIP!

BUT, NO—
TEE-HEE! I LOVE TO PLAY WITH MY TOY BOAT IN THE BATH!
SOAP

THE BEAR FACTS

THE song "Bear Necessities" could have been written with BEANO and DANDY in mind. Bears, big, small, cuddly and grizzly have featured in their pages from the comics' earliest issues.

Biffo the Bear must be regarded as top dog (er, sorry . . . bear) of the comic world with 26 years of BEANO cover appearances under his belt (er, pelt) and despite his long service, Biffo didn't retire when he stepped off the cover in 1974. He was given his own strip inside the comic.

The Biffo story below is from the cover of BEANO issue 16th June, 1962.

NOT to be outdone, DANDY also had its share of bears. A big favourite with readers during the 1950s was **Barney's Bear,** a cute creature who found himself in one fix after another. Trouble always seemed to be brewing for this particular bruin.

In BEANO, there was no risk of **Biffo** becoming lonely, thanks to the long-running adventures of **The Three Bears**. This furry trio spent most of their time searching for food, and this story from 5th March, 1966 is no exception.

Being an outdoor guy means that **Desperate Dan's** met almost as many grizzly bears as he's guzzled cow-pies, but the big man has a soft spot for animals. In fact, he likes bears so much, he once taught some of them to dance.

BARNEY'S BEAR

DRIFTING down the River Rumble on an upturned canoe, Barney's Bear was in trouble as usual. He had got separated from his pals, Barney Brennan and Digger Merry, and once more he was facing the perils of a hard world alone. The river widened out into a shallow lake dotted with islands, for Smarty was in the swamp lands of America. These swamps swarmed with wild things, but Smarty didn't know that He was glad when the canoe drifted alongside a big log lying in the water close to the shore, for he was able to step on to the log and make his way ashore.

2—But he had taken only one step on the log when he felt it roll under him. Looking back over his shoulder in surprise, Smarty was astonished to see the front part of the "log" open up and give out a deep bellow of rage. It wasn't a log at all, but a monster crocodile that had been snoozing in shallow water until Smarty stepped on it! If the cub had worn a shirt, he would have jumped right out of it with fright. As it was, he leaped from the croc's middle on to the bank. His heart was in his mouth—and in another moment it came near to being in the crocodile!

... clashed together only inches from the ... and made ... in the water ... he ... the ... Growling, Sm... bank, a big rus... Clang—crunch...

...ing its mighty tail in fury, the croc edged forward to ...ther ... and wasn't it surprised when it ...pen! The old pot formed as cute ...alive trapper had ever set. But ... was short-lived, for he heard a ... and turned to see an evil head ... a wide-open mouth from which ...him! It was a great big snake

5—Wow! Smarty wheeled around, circled a tree and sped off ... greased lightning. He never had liked snakes, and this was ... The only thing to do was get away ... him over the ground ...

6—The hissing of the snake so close behind ... Bear that he wasn't safe up the pole. In desperation ... one of the guy-ropes and slid down so fast that his paws ... scorched. The snake struck out at him, but the cub was ... range. And now he was safe, for the reptile didn't seem ... Smarty saw that the flagpole ... the guy-rope ... to Catch-'em-Alive Cars...

THREE BEARS

I WONDER HOW I CAN GET SOME GRUB?

THERE'S A LOAD OF BULLY BEEF GOING OUT ON THE NOON DAY TRAIN, ZEKE.
RED GULCH
POP. 300 + 3 BEARS
LUNCH BOX
BULLY BEEF?

BACK AT THE CAVE—
TED, I'LL NEED YOUR GUARD'S UNIFORM TO HELP ME PINCH A LOAD OF BULLY BEEF!
SURE THING, PA.
SPOT

I'M THE NEW GUARD. WE'RE MOVING OFF EARLY TO FOOL ANY BANDITS.
GOOD IDEA!
PA IN DISGUISE

AH! WE'LL SOON BE PASSING THE CAVE!
CHUFF! CHUFF!
TOOT

CHUFF! CHUFF!

SNIGGER! NOW TO UNHOOK THE BULLY BEEF WAGGON!
BULLY BEEF

BYE-BYE, MR ENGINE DRIVER! HEH-HEH!
CHUFF! CHUFF!
BULLY
BEEF

THE PLAN WORKED PERFECTLY, BEARS!
SLURP! LOTS OF LOVELY BULLY BEEF, AND ALL FOR US!

OPEN THE DOOR, TED. WHAT'S IN THERE SHOULD KEEP US GOING FOR AGES!
BULLY
BEEF

BUT—
SNORT! BELLOW!
WOW! THE BULLY BEEF HASN'T BEEN CANNED YET!

GASP! YOU WERE RIGHT, PA! IT WILL KEEP US GOING FOR AGES!

IT'S A DODGER'S LIFE FOR ME!

ALL kids love dodging, whether they're dodging homework, dodging Mum or Dad when some chores need done, or dodging another TV chat show! But most fun of all is reading about the exploits of the world's greatest ever dodger — BEANO star **Roger the Dodger.**

Roger is to dodgers what Maradona is to kids kicking a football around in the park — simply the best.

He's been driving his dad batty since he first appeared in BEANO in 1953, when he dodgered his way into the hearts of millions of crafty readers — everyone of whom would give a year's pocket money (well, two weeks' anyway!) for a glance at Roger's famous books of dodges.

Sadly though, for his millions of fans, Roger would never let even a BEANO reader sneak a look at his famous books of wily wisdom.

But BEANO fans need never despair. The best — and most enjoyable — way to pick up new dodges for yourself has always been to watch the world's greatest dodger in action in BEANO.

Now that's something nobody's ever wanted to dodge!

ROGER the DODGER

Enjoy Roger at his crafty best in this 1961 adventure.

In this 1977 episode, Roger comes up with a great new dodging invention — then wishes he hadn't!

TOP PEOPLE READ THE

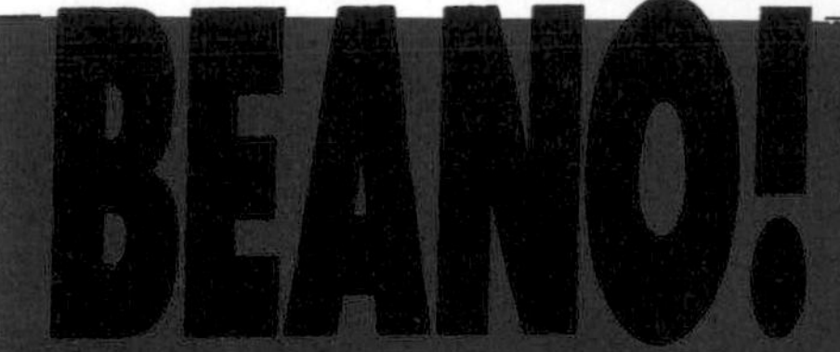

AND our photographer caught some of them enjoying their favourite comic, in a quiet moment away from the glare of the TV lights!

So next time you're having a chuckle at the latest Dennis the Menace adventure, you'll know there's a fair chance that your favourite showbiz stars are doing exactly the same thing!

John Craven keeps up to date with what's happening in his favourite comic.

These stars from TV's popular "Saturday Superstore" know that BEANO's got plenty to crow about!

Comedy actor Geoffrey Palmer takes a break from TV rehearsals — and a quick look at BEANO.

Jimmy Tarbuck not only enjoys reading BEANO — he's also proud to have appeared in this 1983 Lord Snooty adventure.

50 GOLDEN YEARS

YOU'VE read in "DANDY and BEANO At War" how Pansy Potter, Lord Snooty and company did their bit for Britain, but luckily for the war effort, there's one comic character who didn't make his first appearance until 12th November, 1960, long after hostilities were over.

This blundering soldier would have been more help to the enemy than a platoon of their own crack troops.

He's a bone-head, he's a twit, he's as much use as a chocolate kettle, he's . . .

CORPORAL CLOTT

. . . and the blunderful story overleaf is from The DANDY issue of 16th August, 1969.

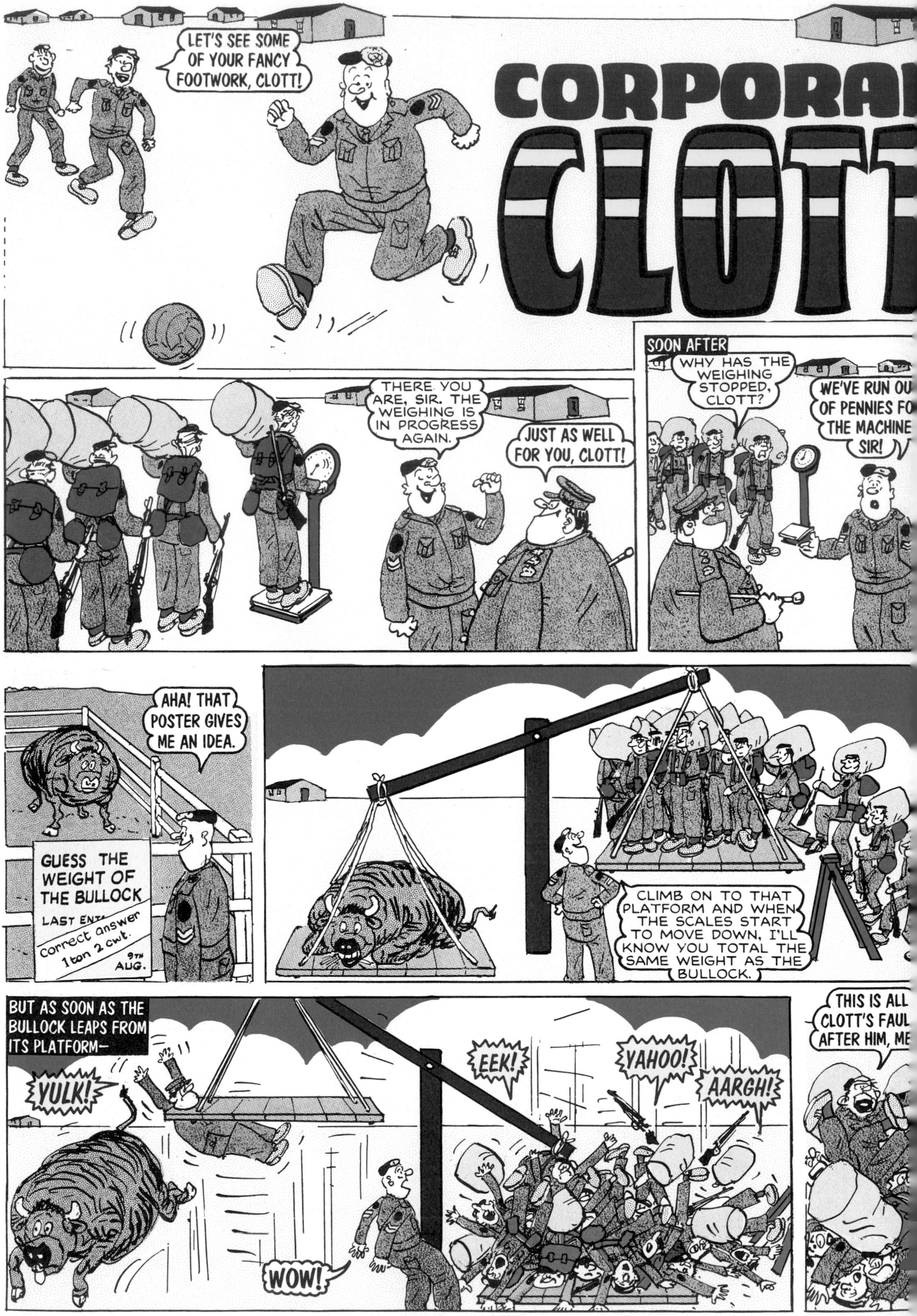

LET'S SEE SOME OF YOUR FANCY FOOTWORK, CLOTT!

CORPORA CLOTT

THERE YOU ARE, SIR. THE WEIGHING IS IN PROGRESS AGAIN.

JUST AS WELL FOR YOU, CLOTT!

SOON AFTER

WHY HAS THE WEIGHING STOPPED, CLOTT?

WE'VE RUN OU OF PENNIES FO THE MACHINE SIR!

WATCH THIS OVER-HEAD KICK! OOPS!

YOU'VE SMASHED OUR ONLY WEIGHING MACHINE, CLOTT! THESE MEN WERE BEING WEIGHED BEFORE BOARDING A PLANE. WHAT ARE WE GOING TO DO NOW?
LEAVE IT TO ME, SIR!

I'VE BORROWED A WEIGHING MACHINE FROM THE CHEMIST'S SHOP, SIR!
ICU2

BAH! WE'LL HAVE TO USE MY BATHROOM SCALES.

THIS JEEP IS GOING ON THE PLANE, TOO! I'LL WEIGH EACH WHEEL SEPARATELY ON THE COLONEL'S SCALES THEN ADD UP THE TOTAL.

AARGH!
YOU NITWIT, CLOTT!
THAT JEEP IS MUCH TOO HEAVY FOR MY SCALES!
ICU2

COME BACK, CLOTT, AND I'LL SMASH YOU, TOO!

THAT'S THE IDEA, MEN! THE SCALES ARE JUST ABOUT TO BALANCE.

WHAT'S THIS BEAST DOING IN MY CAMP? GET IT OUT OF HERE!
BET THIS BULLOCK ISN'T ONE TON TWO HUNDREDWEIGHTS NOW. IT'S LOST SEVERAL POUNDS IN THE CHASE ALREADY!

GRR! CATCH HIM!
HELP! I'VE BEEN FLATTENED!
CHARGE!

The Dandy and the Beano
are very good to read,
To lend and swap and borrow,
so, keep going please, we plead.

Jimmy Savile

DR. JIMMY SAVILE, O.B.E., K.C.S.G. LI.D

On behalf of one hundred million other readers.

NICE ONE JIMMY

SHOWBIZ personality Jimmy Savile is a real action man, finding enough time when he's not appearing on radio or TV to lend a hand at the famous Stoke Mandeville Hospital and enough energy to have a go at marathon running. Phew!

Even so, this real life "Billy Whizz" paused long enough to say some kind words about BEANO and DANDY'S 50th Anniversary — and even put them in rhyme!

Nice one, Jimmy!

D.J. Jimmy goes running with a microphone in his hand!

Here's one BEANO Library we're sure Jimmy would never swap. This 1986 story "Min'll Fix It" starred Jimmy himself!

IN the pages of BEANO and DANDY, schooldays are the happiest years of your life . . . unless you happen to be a TEACHER! These unfortunate members of the teaching profession are targets for paper darts, the victims of tricks and the butt of their pupils' jokes. The kids of the comic world are experts at turning schooldays into . . .

Schooldaze

SCHOOLKIDS can instantly transform almost anything into a deadly weapon. Here are a few items that have become . . .

TEACHERS' PET HATES!

A FOOTBALL!

Not so much soccer as SOCK 'IM when a flying football catches Teacher by surprise.

A BOW, AN ARROW AND A BOXING GLOVE!

Teachers can usually sniff out mischief, but here's one master who wishes that he didn't have a nose for trouble.

A SLEDGE!

Sometimes called a 'sleigh', and that's exactly what this one will do if Teacher doesn't move fast.

A RUNAWAY ROLLER!

Most teachers like compliments, but here's a couple that don't fancy FLATTERY one little bit.

But for Mr Creep, a teacher at Greytowers boarding school, all other pet hates come a poor second to . . .

WINKER WATSON

Often described as "The World's Wiliest Wangler", Winker has been up to more tricks than Arthur Daley and The Artful Dodger put together.

On the next two pages, readers can see the scheming schoolboy and the miserable master in action in a DANDY story from 6th May, 1961.

Creepy, the master, lands in a mess—When he makes Winker wear "fancy dress"!

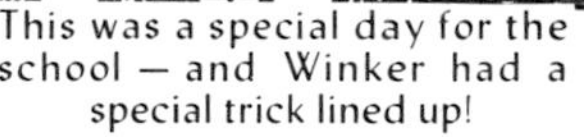
This was a special day for the school — and Winker had a special trick lined up!

But now old Creepy looks like a clown—When his trousers let him down!

Yes! Creepy pursued the mouse along the corridor. Just what Winker wanted!

Wangle accomplished! Creepy had landed in the Head's black books.

But now things looked black for Winker.

However, the wily wangler wasn't worried.

It looked as if Winker's record would be broken.

But no! Creepy's aim was spoiled when he heard his pants suddenly rip.

Ha-ha! Good for Winker! He had weakened the stitching in Creepy's trousers.

And Winker had been busy on the buttons, too!

Creepy's trousers let him down—with a wallop!

—Right in front of the governors! A black mark for Creepy again. This time he was given a punishment.

And that suited Winker and his pals fine. For, with Creepy out of the way, they could wear their old suits again. Good for Winker! He was still top of his Form—at wangling!

BUT when it comes to tormenting teachers, these pupils are the uncrowned champions (it's usually the teacher who gets crowned!). They're reckless, they're rough and they're always ready! They're the . . .

BASH STREET KIDS

Not so much a game for a laugh, as World War Three, when the pupils of Bash Street School challenged their teachers to a rugby match. The masters took on more than they could tackle, and although they didn't score any points they certainly had a trying time.

AND if you think the Bash Street Kids must be better behaved when they're in the classroom, you're in for a big surprise when you read this story from BEANO issue 21st April, 1979.

You'll also meet Cuthbert Cringeworthy, the Teacher's pet, and the kids' pet hate!

TRA-LA-LA!
PAINT STORE
WHITE PAINT
EH-HEH! THIS IS THE STUFF I'M AFTER!

TEACHER WILL BE PLEASED WITH ME.
HARHAR!
DIP
WHITE PAINT

Soon—
ARGH! MY BLACKBOARD'S A WHITEBOARD!
HORRORS!
TITTER! HE WON'T BE ABLE TO WRITE SUMS ON IT NOW!

ERK! WHAT HAVE I DONE?
SMOULDER
DO I SMELL BURNING?

I'VE HEARD OF BURNING QUESTIONS, BUT THIS IS TOO MUCH!

GLURG!
SWOOSH!
CAN'T WRITE ON THAT ANY MORE, TEACHER!

TEE-HEE-HEE! THAT TICKLES!

HOLD STILL, MAN!
WRIGGLE
PLEASE, SIR—WE CAN'T READ THE SUMS—THEY KEEP MOVING!

Presently—
THIS WHAT YOU WANTED, TEACHER?
SPLENDID! THE VERY THING!

Then—
IS THAT BOY EATING? COME OUT HERE!
CHOMP!

JUST WHAT I NEED, GLUTTONOUS YOUTH!

15 19 11 43
21 33 29 13
ALL YOUR FAULT, FAT FREAK!
THIS CHOC WRITES WELL ON MY WHITEBOARD!

IN A CLASS OF THEIR OWN!

THAT'S the kids of **Bash Street School.** Whether it's making Teacher weep or readers chuckle, these kids are tops! Here are a few selected scenes featuring the jokes and japes of the **Bash Street Kidders!**

The Bash Street Kids often make a sucker out of Teacher, but here's one time they were the suckers — except for silly Smiffy — he blew it as usual.

It's not true that the other kids don't play with Cuthbert, the teacher's pet. They once let him join in a game of cricket — as the stumps.

Fatty isn't really greedy. He only ever eats ONE slice of tart at a sitting.

Teacher reckons he's a charming fellow, but he discovered he was no snake charmer when an escaped reptile took refuge in the school.

Teacher thought it was a waste of time when the kids brought a swordfish to school. But the master soon got the point.

Every school has a cloakroom, but one of the kids' tricks provided Bash Street School with its very own CROAKROOM!

Some readers reckon Plug is plug ugly but he thinks he's pretty as a picture.

Cuthbert is such a swot he usually has his nose in a book. And Danny is only too happy to help.

All Teacher wants is peace and quiet! What he usually gets is a riot! But he knows there is one way to keep the kids in their seats and in silence! Pity school books don't have the same effect.

ANOTHER teacher who regularly came a cropper was The DANDY'S **Greedy Pigg.** As his name suggests, this rotund master was rather partial to food. In fact he was a walking waste disposal unit, who wasn't fussy where he found his grub or who he snaffled it from. So most readers reckoned he usually got what he deserved at the end of each story and that wasn't a slap-up meal at The Ritz.

MASTERS OF MIRTH

YOU'VE probably realised by now that the pages of BEANO and DANDY aren't the safest place on earth for teachers, but there was one, way back in The DANDY of 1939, who faced a class of pupils without feeling he'd strayed on to a military firing range by mistake.

Who was this amazing master? Was he an all-in wrestler, a movie stunt-man, a member of the S.A.S.? Nope! This teacher was a **WALRUS.**

When grumpy teacher, Mr Brown, was turned into a walrus by a gypsy's curse, he discovered that problem pupils were the least of his worries.

But Mr Brown's misfortunes were good news for DANDY readers. **Our Teacher's A Walrus** proved to be a very popular story with young comic fans during the early years of World War II.

EDITOR'S WARNING!

Being naughty to teachers is only fun in comics. Copying the antics you've just read about could seriously damage your school report.

ONE MILLION PEOPLE CAN'T BE WRONG!

5TH JUNE, 1976 is a date which should be noted in very large lettering in every history teacher's notebook. It was the date of an event to rival the launch of the first space shuttle or the first ascent of Mount Everest!

The event in question was that great moment in comic history — the launch of The BEANO'S Dennis The Menace Club, to be followed two years later by DANDY'S Desperate Dan Club.

Even if some history teachers may have missed the significance of these dates, very few readers of the two comics did and over the years an incredible one million kids have become members of the two famous clubs. That's enough to fill Wembley Stadium ten times over!

It's also, we suspect, enough to give Dennis the Menace and Desperate Dan writers' cramp, replying to all the members whose letters are printed in the club pages of BEANO and DANDY.

'But what have Dan and Dennis fans got for their membership money?' you may ask and the answer is 'lots' — like a mouthwatering Pie-Eater's club badge and secrets of Dan's muscle-building exercises for Desperate Dan fans and an amazing Gnasher badge for readers who enjoy menacing in Dennis's footsteps.

More info and application forms for anybody who'd like to join one of these famous clubs are available in the weekly comics, but if anybody still has some doubts as to whether the clubs REALLY are worth joining, just consider this — one million people can't be wrong!

DENNIS the MENACE FAN CLUB

Attention, all Menace fans! I've started my very own fan club - and so has Gnasher! I want you all to join! There's a smashing lapel badge, and a fantastic hairy Gnasher badge, too (see below)! Details of how to join my club at foot of page.

DROP ME A LINE Your problems answered by a famous p... child...

Dear Dennis, I have trouble getting up in the morning to go to school. What should I do? Minnie the Minx.

Dear Minnie, Your problems are over - Don't bother getting up! Dennis.

GNASHER'S FANG CL...

Send me a story about your pet

NAME

ADDRE...

JOIN THE DESPERATE DAN PIE-EATER'S CLUB

1 DESPERATE DAN PIE-EATERS CLUB HAND PAINTED 3-D PLASTIC BADGE

ALL MEMBERS WILL RECEIVE FOUR SUPER GIFTS

2 BRIGHTLY COLOURED METAL BADGE

3 MEMBERSHIP CARD, CLUB PASSWORDS AND SECRETS OF DAN'S MUSCLE-BUILDING EXERCISES, ALL IN A SPECIAL CLUB WALLET.

4 SET OF SIX CLUB STICKERS

I LOVE SCHOOL — HOWDY — HI, THERE — I'M A HEE-HEE HE-MAN

We found Mandy's Mum asleep on a deck-chair one day, so we tied our dog's lead to the chair.

The dog was a greyhound and it was desperately strong. When Mandy called it, it bounded across the garden pulling the deck-chair behind it! Even Mandy's Mum laughed at the trick.

—Jackie Martin and Mandy West, Tunbridge Wells.

DAN says—

I'd pick this pooch to beat The Beano's Gnasher any day!

My sister loves apricots, and she made a cake decorated with apricot halves.

Well, I put a raw egg yolk in a dish then called her to come and get the apricot that was left over.

She swallowed it before learning about the trick. And then she was nearly sick!

—Jerome Mee, Four Roads, Co. Roscommon.

My younger brother came into the lounge dressed in my Dad's old boots and waistcoat.

"I'm Desperate Dan," he growled.

"Yes, and I'm Bully Beef," my Dad replied and clipped his ear. Next moment my dog jumped up as if to say "And I'm Black Bob!"

—Ian Cole, Notting...

Stopping to watch a mechanical digger clearing away rubble in the street, my sister asked me what the digger was called.

"A caterpillar," I told her.

You should have seen my Mum's ... when my sist... she'd ...

THE Dandy
Nº 2000!
SPECIAL CELEBRATION ISSUE!
7p
No. 2000
March 22nd, 1980.
EVERY TUESDAY
KORKY the CAT
WHAT'S THAT YOU'VE GOT THERE, KORKY?
THIS IS THE BIRTHDAY CAKE FOR THE DANDY'S 2000TH ISSUE! I'M GOING TO HAVE A PARTY!
THE GAMEY DIDN'T KNOW THESE ARE SPECIAL CANDLES. I JUST FIT THEM TOGETHER, SO—
AND THEY MAKE A SMASHING FISHING ROD!
NO FISHING
LATER—
HEY! HAVE YOU BEEN FISHING?
FISHING? HOW COULD I WITHOUT A ROD?
TO THE RIVER
HEE-HEE! THE GAMEY WOULD HAVE A FIT IF HE KNEW THE SECRET OF THIS CAKE!
IT'S HOLLOW—AND LOOK WHAT I HID INSIDE IT!
HAPPY BIRTHDAY TO ME— AND TO THE DANDY!

GREAT MOMENTS IN HISTORY

HISTORY teachers may struggle to teach their pupils about great events in history (especially if they're facing the Bash Street Kids!), but here's one date most kids will have no trouble recalling.

It came in 1980 when BEANO and DANDY each celebrated their **2000th issue**.

50 GOLDEN YEARS

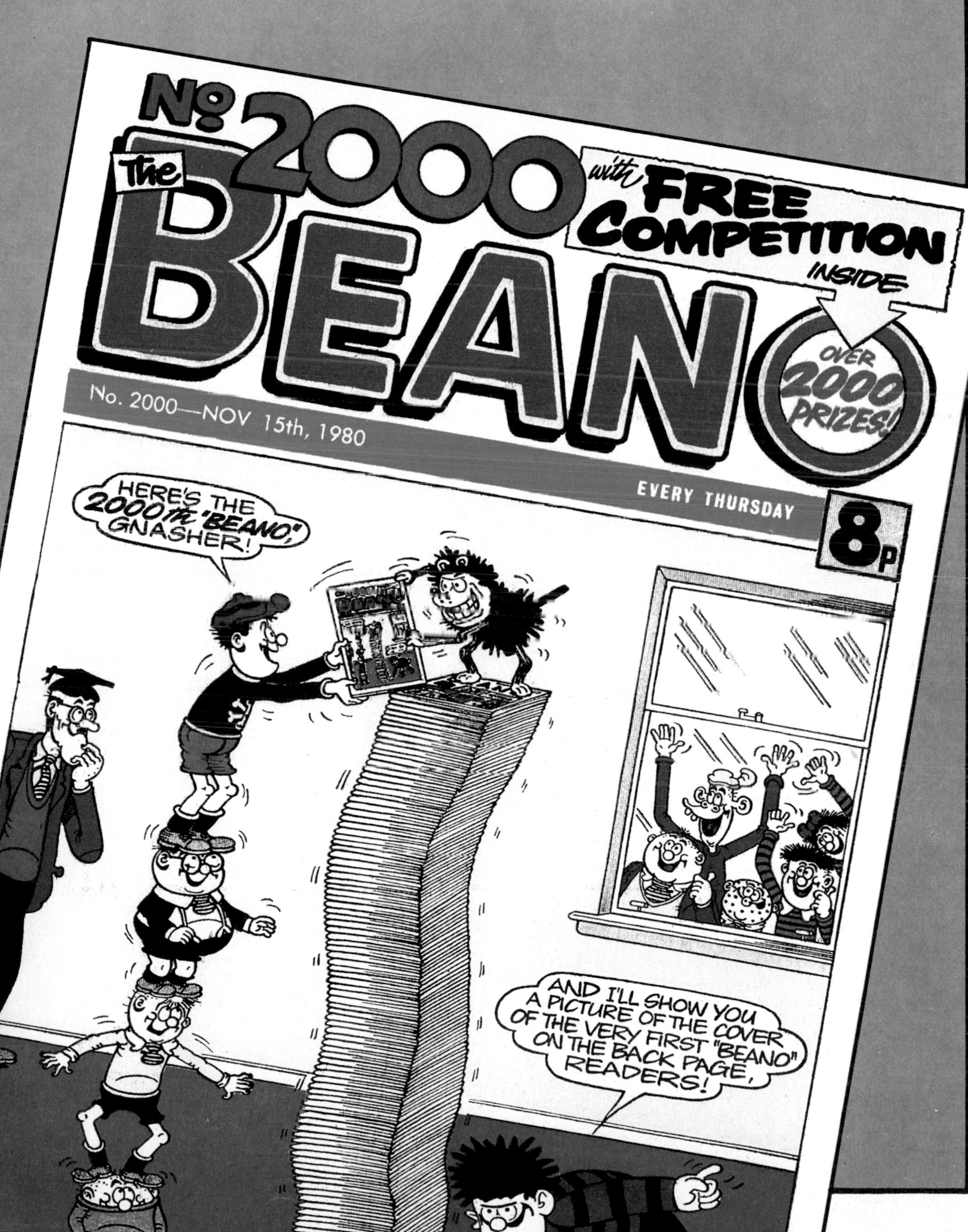

LUKE WHO'S HERE

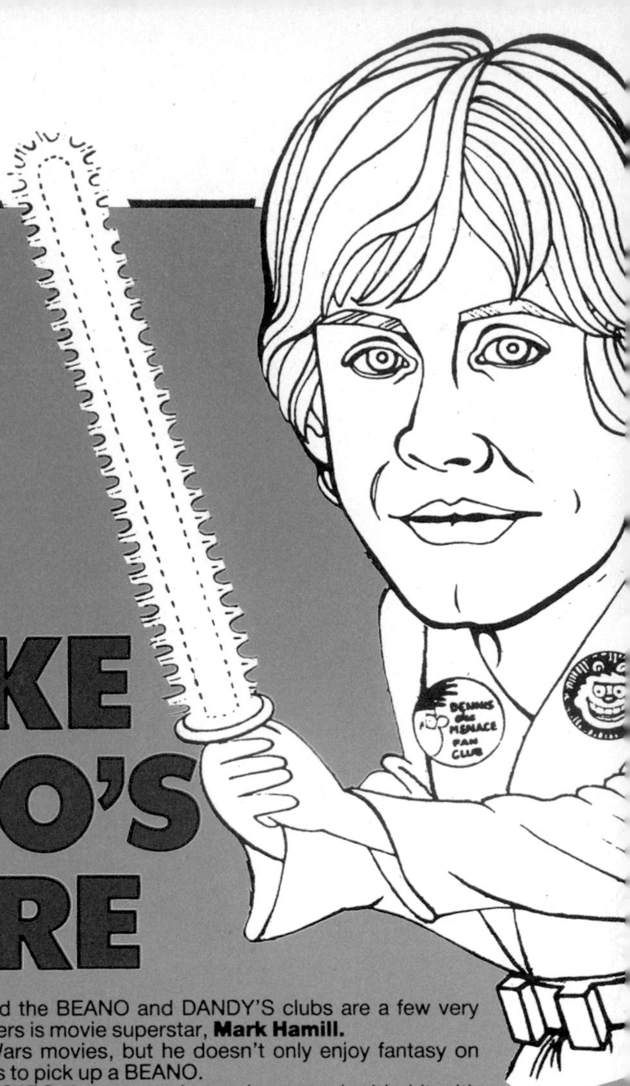

AMONG the million plus comic fans who've joined the BEANO and DANDY'S clubs are a few very familiar names, and one of those celebrity members is movie superstar, **Mark Hamill.**

Mark portrayed **Luke Skywalker** in the Star Wars movies, but he doesn't only enjoy fantasy on the big screen. When he's not working, Mark likes to pick up a BEANO.

Two of Mark's most famous co-stars are R2D2 and C3PO the crazy robots who proved a big hit with movie audiences. And sharing the screen with those robots probably reminded comic-fan Mark of the many metal characters that have appeared in the pages of BEANO and DANDY.

An entire metal menagerie has been featured over the last fifty years — a clockwork horse, an iron fish and a clanking dog have all entertained readers, along with a metal maid, a butler held together with rivets and a whole host of robots.

In fact there have been so many robot stories in the comics that someone once suggested that The BEANO and DANDY editors should go into the scrap metal business.

The undisputed metal megastar of the comic world is DANDY'S **Brassneck,** the robot schoolboy who made his first appearance on 5th December, 1964.

With his flesh and blood pal, Charley Brand, Brassneck has been in more scrapes than a stock car with wonky steering. The adventure overleaf is from 24th July, 1965.

Here's a tale to make you grin — Of a wild and woolly metal Redskin!

Charley and Brassneck had been so thrilled by the film that they went home and dressed up to have their own game of cowboys and Indians.

HO-HO! THAT SUITS YOU, BRASSNECK!

What an uproar of "YOWS!" — When Brassneck visits a picture house.

WHAT'S GLOSSY ON THE OUTSIDE? PACKED WITH FUN ON THE INSIDE? AND READ ALL OVER?

NO prizes for guessing that the answer is The DANDY and BEANO Comic Libraries.

The perfect buy for kids who enjoy a BIG laugh, each comic features one long story starring one of the most popular characters from the famous weekly publications — with occasional guest appearances from stars from other comics.

What's more, as the name suggests, these special BEANOS and DANDYS build up to a library of humour for their fans, which make a very attractive collection for readers' bookshelves, especially for anybody who has bought each one since the BEANO Library was first published in 1982 and the DANDY Library in 1983.

Collectability — that's the beauty of The DANDY and BEANO Comic Libraries!

HEAP BIG STARS

STARQUOTE

"It was always our ambition to appear in either The Beano or Dandy, but we've never been big enough stars to compete with Dennis The Menace, The Bash Street Kids and all the other megastars who made our childhood days so happy."

WITH apologies to Eddie Large, we'd like to remind you of the old saying that the best things come in small packages — like two of the world's top 'funnymen' Syd Little and Little Plum!

But size apart, Syd and his partner Eddie are both heap big stars — one of the funniest comedy duos in the business and both big fans of that other famous comedy duo, BEANO and DANDY!

SYD ONCE GOT IN THE BEANO AS A STAPLE (HE WAS ON A STAPLE DIET AT THE TIME!!) AND HAS NEVER STOPPED READING IT. EVEN TODAY HE TELLS GAGS THAT HE'S READ IN THE BEANO (SO DO I, COME TO THINK OF IT!). WHEN HE WAS A PAPER BOY HE ALWAYS USED TO READ THE BEANO AND DANDY BEFORE PUSHING THEM THROUGH THE LETTERBOXES.

EDDIE ALWAYS REMINDS ME OF DESPERATE DAN, ONLY HE'S NOT SO GOOD LOOKING! WE USED TO HAVE FUN READING THE BEANO AND DANDY OUT LOUD AND GIVING THE CHARACTERS VOICES THAT WE THOUGHT FITTED THEM.

HEAP FUNNY INDIAN

KIDS everywhere just love playing cowboys and Indians, so not surprisingly there have been lots of Wild West heroes over the years. Few have been bigger stars though than a pint-sized Indian who has won the hearts of generations of BEANO readers.

He is, of course, **Little Plum,** the heap funny Indian who has been a BEANO star since way back in 1953.

This ad from BEANO issued dated 3rd October, 1953 announced the arrival of a great new comic character . . . and thirty years later, Plum was still going strong!

MORE LAUGHS FOR TWOPENCE NEXT THURSDAY!

Two great new funsters will be in your "Beano."

MATT HATTER—
the joker with the world's funniest collection of hats.

LITTLE PLUM—
the Redskin "Dennis."

ALSO

Roger the Dodger will appear in colour!

HEAP FUNNY INDIAN

THE two Plum pages shown here feature our hero on both sides of the Atlantic.

In the first, we see Plum's 1980 visit to London, a great event happily recorded by a photographer.

In the second, Plum is back home in America, providing plenty of laughs when he tries to discover if smoke signals are the best way to send um message.

YOUR INDIAN PAL VISITS LONDON

LITTLE PLUM

I HAVEN'T HAD UM CHAT WITH LITTLE BEAVER OF UM SOREFEET TRIBE FOR UM WHILE.

SO—
I'M USING UM TRADITIONAL INDIAN FORM OF COMMUNICATION— SMOKE SIGNALS!
WAFT

THEN—
HEY! WE'VE BEEN CUT OFF!

TUT, TUT! DON'T YOU KNOW THIS IS UM SMOKELESS ZONE?

PRESENTLY—
MUST CLEAN UM CARPET!
MM!
SUCK!

AND—
THERE!
SUCK
BLOW

DUST
GET UM IDEA, READERS?
BRR!
BLOW

BUT DUST IS HEAVIER THAN AIR—
COUGH! SPLUTTER!

SO—
?
BOIL

THANKS, PLUM. I COULD DO WITH UM CUP OF TEA.
HUH! I'LL NEED TO TRY SOMETHING ELSE!

SO—
I'LL USE THE STEAM FROM THIS HOT GEYSER!
OLD FACE-FULL

THEN—
BAH!

SOME OF THESE OLD INDIAN TRADITIONS ARE BEST FORGOTTEN!
Dear Little Beaver, I am writing to you

ANOTHER FINE MESS

. . . And another . . . and another! In fact, when BEANO'S **Smudge** and **Dirty Dick** from DANDY were around, there was usually nothing but mess! These two could end up looking black in a talcum powder factory.

Smudge, seen on the left proving that even writing can be a dirty job, started his comic career on 19th April, 1980.

Dirty Dick however is a real veteran of rubbish tips and mud baths, first appearing in DANDY issue, 15th October, 1960. He's seen below in a typically messy tale.

HAVE A GIGGLE WITH THE GIRLS!

THEY'RE tougher than Desperate Dan (well, almost) craftier than Roger the Dodger (nearly) more menacing even than **Dennis** (well, maybe!) — they're the girls who star in the pages of BEANO and DANDY!

One thing these girls definitely are NOT is sugar 'n' spice and all things nice, as lots of boys have discovered when they've been mangled by **Minnie the Minx** or pulverised by **Pansy Potter.**

But whether it's Mum, Dad or the boy down the street who's being out-thought, out-minxed or outraged by these comic heroines, you can be sure that plenty of laughs are provided on the way for lucky readers of the two famous comics.

So why not flick over the next page or two and have a giggle with the girls?

A comic star with a difference, DANDY's **Keyhole Kate** proved she wasn't just the nosiest girl around — but one of the funniest too!

Desperate Dan and Cactusville go together like fish and chips, but during the forties the township had another famous inhabitant, BEANO's **Ding Dong Belle.**

Who needs brakes to stop a speeding car? Certainly not DANDY strong girl **Pansy Potter!**

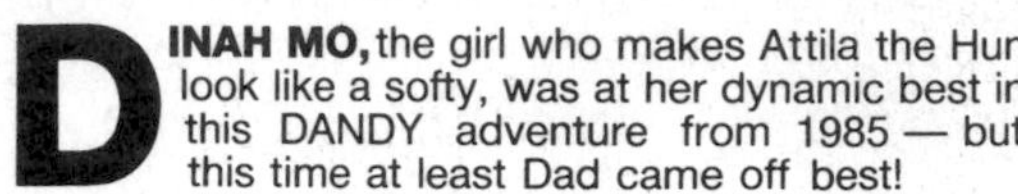

DINAH MO, the girl who makes Attila the Hun look like a softy, was at her dynamic best in this DANDY adventure from 1985 — but this time at least Dad came off best!

NOW FOR A BIT OF TARGET PRACTICE!

THUD!
HOI!
TWANG!

WHO DID THAT? THERE'S NOBODY IN SIGHT BUT A NICE LITTLE GIRL WITH A HANDBAG!

Later—
I'VE BEEN HEARING ABOUT YOU! TURN OUT THAT BAG!
ULP! DAD!
KEEP EMPTYING!

I THOUGHT SO! NOTHING BUT TROUBLE!
GULP!

NOW I HAVE SOMETHING TO SHOW YOU!
I DON'T THINK I'LL LIKE THIS!

YOU'RE GOING TO NEED YOUR HANDBAG TO CARRY SOOTHING OINTMENT!
EEK! MERCY!

MINNIE made her first appearance in BEANO shortly before Christmas in 1953 and to her dad's horror, she's been minxing ever since!

This adventure appeared in BEANO issue dated November 10th, 1984.

MINNIE the MINX

BAAA! BAAA! BAAA!
EH? WHAT'S THAT NOISE?

THAT'S FINE—I NEED 46 SHEEP OVER THE WALL, THEN I'LL SUBTRACT 19 OF THEM!
STOP! STOP! STOP! MY LOVELY GARDEN!
LEAP

YOUR DAUGHTER SAID THEY WERE WELCOME TO GRAZE IN THERE.
DAD WON'T BE ABLE TO STAND MUCH MORE OF THIS!
BUT I DIDN'T!

Soon—
I WON'T ANNOY YOU WITH THIS CALCULATOR, DAD - IT'S SILENT.
GOOD, MIN.

IT'S A BUCKET OF SAND, SO I CAN COUNT THE GRAINS!
URGH!
FLUMP!

THE MESS! THE NEW CARPET! THAT DOES IT!
ARE YOU GOING TO BUY ME A NEW CALCULATOR?

NO—I'M GOING TO HELP YOU COUNT, WITH THE USE OF THIS SLIPPER!
I DIDN'T COUNT ON THIS!
GOSH! THIS BAG'S HEAVY.

OH, DEAR! WHAT'VE I BROKEN?
CRUNCH!

I'VE SMASHED YOUR CALCULATOR, MIN. GO AND GET YOURSELF A NEW ONE.
GREAT!

DAD! YOU'RE NOT GOING TO MIX CEMENT ON THE CARPET! I WON'T STAND FOR IT!
B-B-BUT...

SOMETIMES DAD CAN BE SO BAD TEMPERED FOR NO REASON AT ALL.
PAH!
IF ONLY SHE KNEW!
GRIND

DURING the 1970's both BEANO and DANDY came up with popular comic heroines.

Dumb Belle, as the title of her story suggests, was never likely to win a mastermind title, but when it came to making readers chuckle, this particular DANDY character was a real winner!

As for BEANO's **Sweet Sue,** lots of boys discovered that tangling with this particular demure young miss was like tweaking a tiger's tale!

SWEET SUE
NOISE!
BLARE!
EXCUSE ME, WOULD YOU MIND TURNING YOUR TRANSISTOR DOWN? I'M TRYING TO READ.
MORE NOISE!
GET LOST, LITTLE GIRL—IT'S NOT LOUD ENOUGH YET!
NOT STRAINING
GO AND PLAY YOUR RADIO SOMEWHERE ELSE, NASTY BOY!
GLUB!
THERE! NOW I CAN GET A LITTLE PEACE.
GROWL! SNARL! DISPLEASED NOISES!
GOSH, THIS IS AN INTERESTING BOOK!
EH? WHAT'S HAPPENING?
WHIZZZ-Z!
YIKES!
CASUAL
INTERESTING THOUGH IT IS, THAT BOOK IS NOT FOR ME . . .
THUD!
GIBBER! GIBBER! HOW DID SHE DO IT?
...JUDO IS TOO ROUGH A SPORT FOR LITTLE GIRLS.
ALL ABOUT JUDO

When ordinary schoolboy, little Eric, eats a banana — he instantly becomes the EXTRA-ordinary . . .

BANANAMAN

This high-flying star of DANDY has his own TV cartoon series and the strength of 20 men (20 big men). He also has more biceps than brains, which means as many long laughs as daring deeds in his adventures. But every exciting story needs both heroes and villains, so let's meet . . .

. . . THE GOODIES

Top TV funnymen **Bill Oddie, Graham Garden** and **Tim Brooke-Taylor,** better known as The Goodies, provide the hilarious voices for the Bananaman TV cartoon films.

. . . AND THE BADDIES

General Blight (he's the one in the natty green uniform) is **Bananaman's** number one enemy. The villain is seen here briefing **Doctor Gloom.** Blight wants his henchmen to use his hi-tech weapons to attack Bananaman.

Er, it looks as if **Gloom** couldn't find any of his latest Bananaman-blasting gadgets. He's had to settle for something simpler.

But it isn't always blunders when our hero's around. Here he is rounding up the evil . . . well, slightly naughty gang, **The Heavy Mob.**

And talking of news — here's some great news for all Bananafans. There are two hilarious pages featuring Bananaman overleaf from The DANDY of 30th August, 1986.

BANANAMAN

BLACK HOLES ARE FOUND IN SPACE, PUPILS. THINGS VANISH INTO THEM.

SOUNDS JUST LIKE FATTY'S MOUTH!

HEY! WHERE'S ALL THIS STUFF GOING?
I'LL FOLLOW AND SEE!

A BLACK HOLE! I BET THAT'S WHERE THE SATELLITE HAS GONE. BUT IF I GO IN THERE, HOW WILL I GET OUT AGAIN?

INDIAN RESTAURANT
BLACK HOLE OF CALCUTTA
PITY I'M GOING A BIT TOO FAST FOR A VINDALOO TAKEAWAY!

AND THERE'S THE MISSING SATELLITE!

I SAY! WHAT WAS THAT BANG?
BOOM!

ERIC — I SAY, ERIC — ER . . .
ANOTHER JOB WELL DONE — IT'S LUCKY WE DON'T HAVE BLACK HOLES ON EARTH, ISN'T . . .

WOW! LOOK AT THAT!
DAILY WHINE
SATELLITE GOES MISSING IN SPACE

THIS IS A JOB FOR...

FAZOOSH!

...BANANAMAN. AND THAT'S ME, FOLKS!

AHA! THIS IS JUST WHAT I NEED.

IT'S PERFECT FOR POT-HOLING — OR BLACK-HOLING, IN MY CASE!
NO PARKING

WELL, APART FROM THE LONG HAUL HOME, THAT'S THE JOB FINISHED.

Back on Earth —
YOUR SATELLITE, GENERAL — SAFE AND SOUND.
THANKS, BANANAMAN! WE'LL TRY NOT TO LOSE IT AGAIN!

AAIEE!
I DID TRY TO WARN HIM!

OH, MOAN! OH, GROAN!
I THOUGHT YOU SAID WE DIDN'T HAVE ANY BLACK HOLES ON EARTH, ERIC?

TOM, DICK AND SALLY AND JOAN

Recording star **Joan Armatrading** has enjoyed lots of great moments in her career, such as hit records, and successful TV and concert appearances.

But two top moments in Joan's life were nothing at all to do with showbusiness, and everything to do with BEANO and DANDY!

The first was in 1983 when Joan appeared in the **Tom, Dick and Sally** strip on this page. The second was when she visited the BEANO and DANDY offices to see where her favourite comics are produced.

Even Dennis the Menace was on his best behaviour that day!

STARQUOTE

When I was a young girl, I was a great fan of DANDY and BEANO and collected a huge pile of comics. Unfortunately my mum threw them out without telling me and in recent years I've had to spend pounds in collectors' shops buying the same comics that cost me a few pennies when I was a kid.

Dennis the Menace and Little Plum are two of my favourite characters, but most of all I like Tom, Dick and Sally because I appeared in a story with them once!

LOOKING JUST DANDY (AND BEANO)

NOT content with conquering the comic world, BEANO and DANDY have made their mark in the fashion stakes as well!

Girls, it seems, not only enjoy reading about the exploits of Minnie the Minx and Desperate Dan — they also enjoy dressing up like their comic heroes and heroines.

This classy fashion spread appeared in the popular JACKIE magazine in November, 1983 and itself proved very popular with readers who at long last could impress their friends with the BEANO and DANDY look!

COMIC CUTS

MINNIE THE MINX

DENNIS THE MENACE

BERYL THE PERIL

LORD SNOOTY

DESPERATE DAN

CAN YOU SPOT THE DIFFERENCE BETWEEN A BEANO AND DANDY READER?

Turn the page to find out . . .

EVERYTHING'S COMING UP

BANANA bags to colouring books, pencil cases to paper plates, they've all featured top characters from BEANO or DANDY over the years. Even the most everyday object it seems can become a great attraction for kids when that special COMICal touch is added.

T-shirts and jerseys, for instance, become something to show off proudly to your best pals if they feature top comic characters like **Desperate Dan** or **Dennis the Menace!**

Those modelled here by four enthusiastic DANDY and BEANO readers proved hugely popular not only with them, but with thousands of readers, when they became available as prizes for kids lucky enough to have their letters printed in their favourite comics.

As for the other goodies with the special DANDY or BEANO flavour, most have been for sale at some time or other to fans of the two famous comics, who've proved time and time again that they just can't get enough of their favourite comics.

As our pictures show, everything's coming up BEANO and DANDY!

DANDY fan SHONA bubbles with enthusiasm as she models this fetching Desperate Dan T-shirt.

BEANO fan DAVID, sporting a smashing Dennis jersey, proves that he can menace with the best of them!

Looking at billboards became great fun for BEANO fans when Smarties ran this very special advertising campaign some time back.

Lucky DANDY enthusiasts have had lots of great reasons for parting with their pocket money — including these smashing notebooks, jigsaw and bubble bath.

BEANO AND DANDY

50 GOLDEN YEARS

Well, were you right? (A glance at their clothing gives you the answer). To tell the truth though, all four kids assure us they love BOTH comics!

DANDY club member ROSS sets out to prove that he's as strong as Bananaman. We're not about to argue!

More menacing, this time from BEANO fan STEVEN. When he's holding that ruler, everybody ducks!

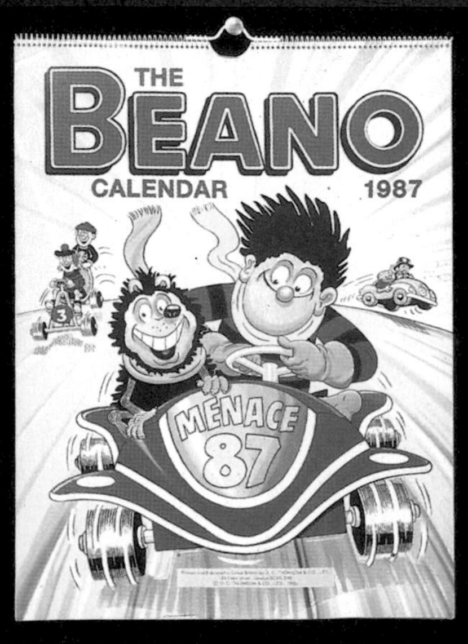

BEANO calendars proved an instant hit with readers who enjoyed menacing their way through the year!

Bananaman, TV star and DANDY star, popped up on lots of goodies, to the delight of his many fans.

50 GOLDEN YEARS

When comics have been around as long as BEANO and DANDY, there are bound to be lots of old favourites amongst their many characters, but it's worth remembering that even stars like Dennis, Korky, and Desperate Dan were new arrivals on the comic scene once upon a time.

Now let's meet a few recent additions to the fun-packed pages of BEANO and DANDY — new faces, who one day may also find a place in the Comics Hall Of Fame.

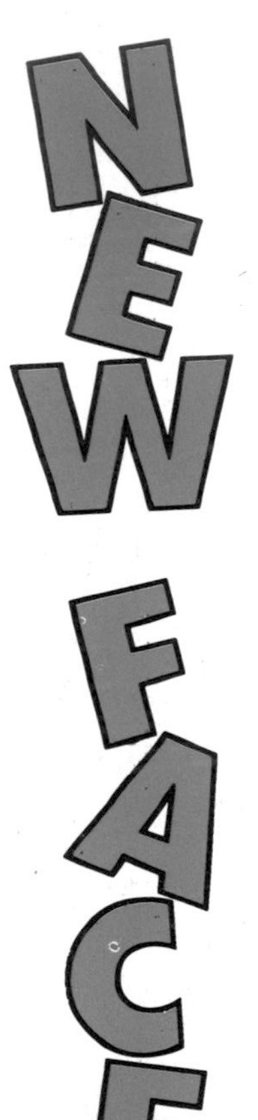

Ivy The Terrible — her name says it all, and this story on the right, from BEANO issue, 8th November, 1986, shows just how terrible Ivy can be.

A STAR IS BORN . . .

. . . And this is how it happened! The BEANO editor suggested a new character to one of his artists, and here we see the artist's first rough sketches for the page which eventually became Calamity James.

Below is the finished article, which BEANO readers saw in issue dated 1st November, 1986.

CUDDLES and DIMPLES
GREAT FUN!
BOING!
GERROFF THE BED, YOU LITTLE— GLUB!
SPLOSH!
BASH!
ROUND TO MY PLACE!
CRASH!
HELP!
COO-EE! I'M HOME!
PLAY WIV TOYS!
CLUNK!
BONK!
TORTURE KIT
BOOM!
PARP!
STOP THIS RACKET!
BUT WHY?
COS IT'S ONLY SEVEN IN THE MORNING!

DANDY fans have voted these two new boys a big hit in every sense of the word. They're Cuddles and Dimples, a couple of tiny terrors, who usually prove more than a match for their poor parents. This story from 22nd November, 1986, is no exception.

HOW WOULD YOU LIKE IT IF WE MADE A LOT OF NOISE?
YOU USUALLY DO, WINDBAG!
BOOM!
TOOT!
STOMP!
WHO CAN THAT BE?
KNOCK! KNOCK!
YOUR RACKET HAS WOKEN THE WHOLE STREET UP!
OH, DEAR!
DON'T DO IT AGAIN!
BIFF!
AND YOU!
BOOT!
COO! WALLOPIES!
CRUNCH!
GROAN!
YOU SHOULD FOLLOW THE EXAMPLE OF YOUR CHILDREN! SUCH SWEET, QUIET BOYS!

YOU'VE read all about DANDY and BEANO'S first fifty years, but what will your favourite comic stars be doing 50 years from now?

Flying their private spaceships on a surprise visit to Dennis's very own space station, perhaps?

There's only one way to find out. Keep reading the comics!

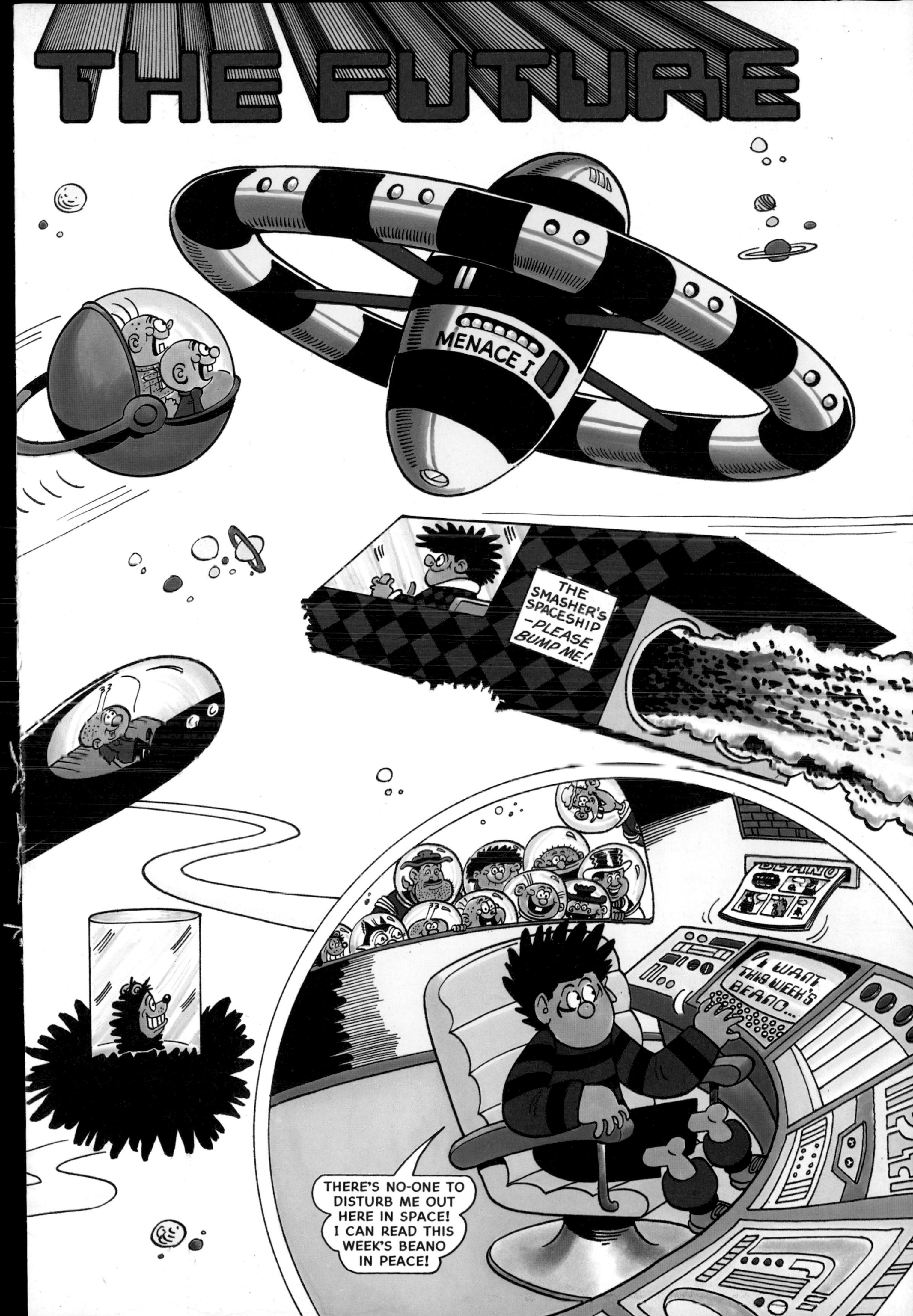
THE FUTURE
MENACE I
THE SMASHER'S SPACESHIP —PLEASE BUMP ME!
I WANT THIS WEEK'S BEANO...
THERE'S NO-ONE TO DISTURB ME OUT HERE IN SPACE! I CAN READ THIS WEEK'S BEANO IN PEACE!

TIN-CAN TOMMY
PODGE
RIP VAN WINK
HUNGRY HORACE
WILD BOY
BIG EGGO
THE SHIPWRECKED CIRCUS
"BABY-FACE" FINLAYSON
ROGER the DODGER
MINNIE the MINX
BUCKTOOTH
THE BOY WHO LIVES IN A BARREL
BRASSNECK